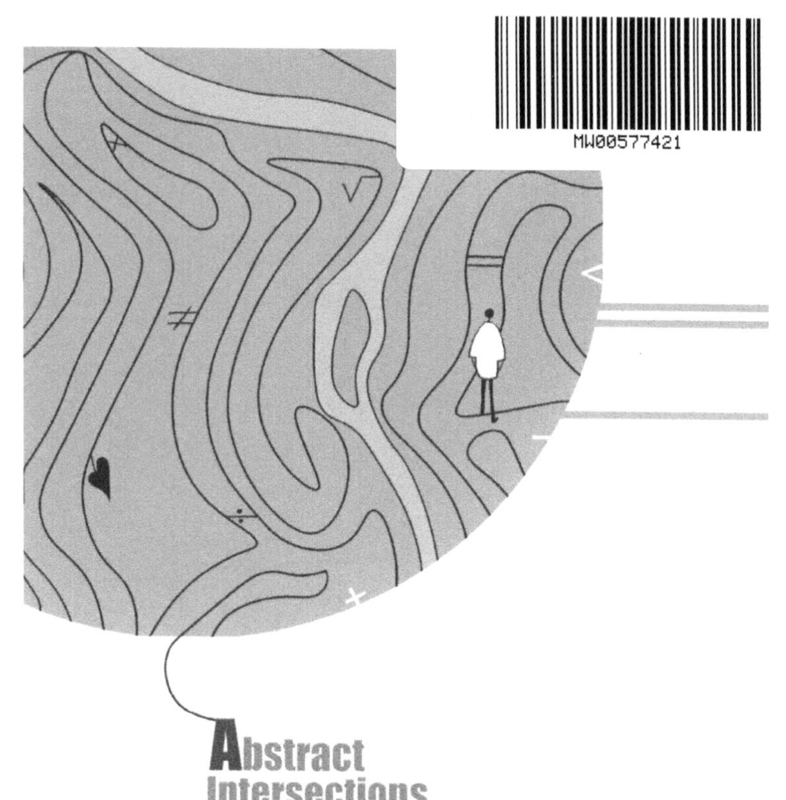

Abstract Intersections

A poetic journey through mathematics

Kedar Hardikar, Ph.D

3490 Notre Dame Dr, Santa Clara,
CA 95051
abstractintersections@gmail.com

Cover design & layouts
Mr. Satish Bhavsar
Mobile: +91 9619043648

November, 2020

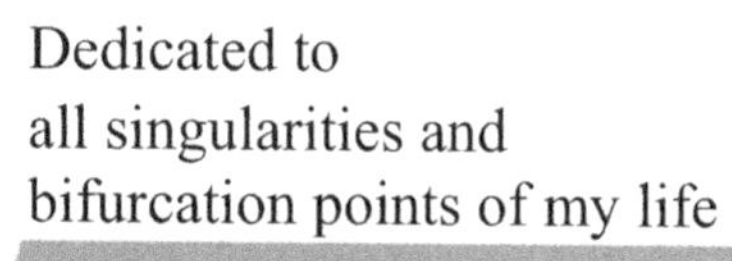

Dedicated to
all singularities and
bifurcation points of my life

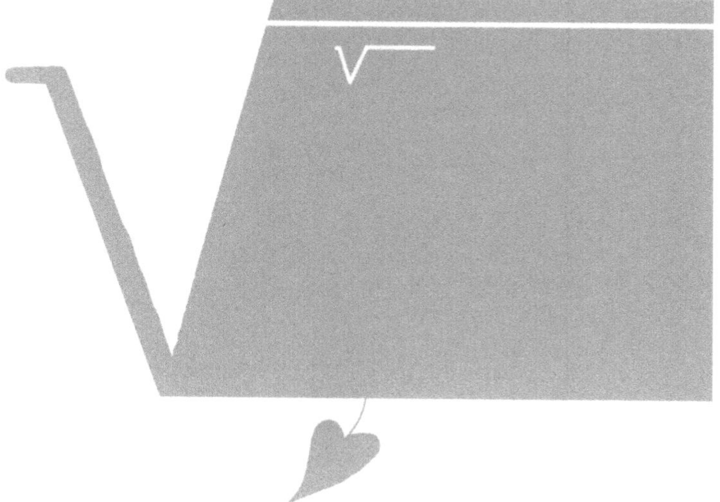

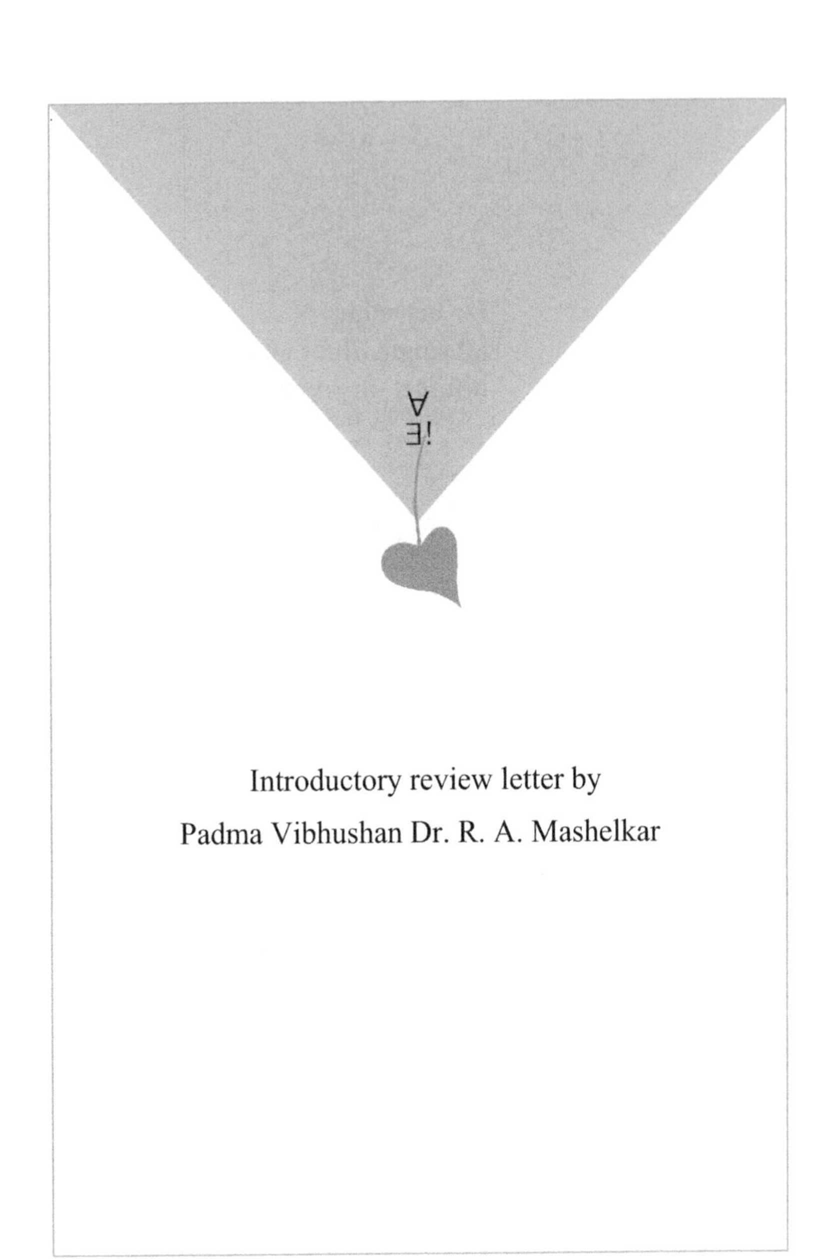

Introductory review letter by

Padma Vibhushan Dr. R. A. Mashelkar

Introductory Review Letter from
Padma Vibhushan Dr. R. A. Mashelkar
Sept 13, 2020

Dear Kedar,

My weekend was well spent in reading and enjoying your book. Here are my thoughts.

Right from my school days, I found it fascinating how mathematics and poetry are both formats that can convey multiple meanings. I found early on how in mathematics, a single object or an idea can take different forms. I saw how a quadratic equation could be understood in algebraic form and its graph, a parabola. Likewise, I was fascinated to see how poets created layers of meaning by utilizing words and images with multiple interpretations and associations.

There was another point I admired. Both mathematicians and poets strived for economy and precision, selecting exactly the words they needed to convey their meaning. Therefore, when you used the term 'mathematical poems,' it did not surprise me; in fact, I welcomed it.

So, I looked at your book as an innovative experiment in mathematical poems. Secondly, I find that 'connecting' the dots is far more challenging than merely 'collecting' the dots. Therefore, I was very impressed with how you have created interesting connections between some celebrated theorems and concepts, both elementary and advanced, in mathematics and life experiences.

Your narrative of the mathematical context that came from the learning and internalization and emotional inspiration that came from a living experience makes an interesting read. Finally, a thought that occurred to me as a result of reading your book is the following. It will be interesting to use poetry in mathematics classes to help students connect emotionally to mathematics. That will surely enable them to think of mathematics as a shared human experience.

Based on your amazing experiential learnings, it will be interesting for the reader to have some of your insights about how through innovation in mathematics teaching, it can be made an enjoyable experience rather than a frightful drudgery.

Congratulations, Kedar, for your wonderful gift to the scientific community and, indeed, to the society.

Warm personal regards,

- R. A. Mashelkar

▲

Mathematics deals with abstract objects and relationships. It is Plato's heaven of ideal forms. Kedar Hardikar was once a graduate student of pure mathematics (that is when I taught him).Then he went out into the real world, with all its angst and pain, its imprecision and uncertainties, and was lost to pure mathematics. But something strange and wonderful seems to have happened: his inner life of deeply felt emotions continued to be molded in shapes provided by the Platonic mathematical forms of his youth! The poems that he has penned are born out of this unlikely marriage. They use Mathematics as a mirror and a powerful metaphor for a surprising range of emotions and moods. After each poem, his notes tell the lay reader just that modicum of mathematics needed to understand the poem. The poems are marvelous -- I greatly enjoyed reading them!

Prof. Nitin Nitsure
School of Mathematics,
Tata Institute of Fundamental Research, Mumbai, India.

Kedar brings the vocabulary of mathematical ideas to the fore in the domain of poetry, introducing novel metaphors for exploring life experiences. To someone like me who is familiar with these concepts, but is not a mathematician, the poems are a revelation into how the language of mathematics can talk beyond equations, and sometimes even express complex emotions. Kedar is a wordsmith who uses both rhyme and reason to try making sense of the irrationality of human life. The full appreciation of the poems needs familiarity with some mathematical concepts, and the format of following each poem with the relevant mathematical background works wonderfully. Those who are already interested in mathematics will no doubt find the poems enjoyable, but I expect many others will be intrigued by the poetry, and a window showing the beauty of mathematics would be open before them.

Prof. Amol S. Dighe
Dept. of Theoretical Physics
Tata Institute of Fundamental Research, Mumbai, India.
(Shanti Swarup Bhatnagar Award Recipient 2013)

With "Abstract Intersections," Dr. Kedar Hardikar has indeed added a rare gem to the genre of math inspired poetry. These unique verses explore the many common unfolding experiences of life through the lens of mathematical ideas. The author's reflections on his own life offer the bedrock for his composition, but most will relate easily to them. The array of topics is bewildering in its diversity and provides a cherishing experience for all. The verses are beautiful, entertaining, and worthy of contemplation. Requiring only a modest background in mathematics this work provides ample treasure to make one ponder. Also, having spent my earlier years with pure mathematics, it is clear that many delights await that will surprise even the professional mathematician.

Prof. Satyajit Karnik
Faculty of Finance, Sheller College of Business
Georgia Institute of Technology, Atlanta, Georgia

▲

Preface

I am neither a professional mathematician nor an accomplished poet. Yet, I find myself writing this preface and contemplating publication of this book. At this moment, life has suggested that I try.

I did not have a specific kind of reader for whom this book was being written. However, I have met quite a few who provided enough encouragement to undertake writing this book. If there is indeed a reader who enjoys these excursions – if that set is "nonempty" – then I consider this endeavor a success. It is indeed one of the strange intersections where I had been standing for a long time – an intersection of mathematics and poetry. It feels as if some fog has cleared. I have some clearer vision that the journey to this beautiful intersection and experience of being at this intersection with changing seasons over decades is of significance, sufficient to attempt writing this book.

My journey started when I was in 11th grade when I was, for the first time, conscious of all the emotional reactions to my learning experience in mathematics. Even in high school, I had emotional reactions to all my learning –science, mathematics, language, or clay modeling. However, I had not distinguished between emotions associated with success or failure and emotions outside of that metric, directly associated with the subject matter. This was true, particularly when it came to science and mathematics. I felt that I was being trained to ignore my liking of objects such as the obtuse isosceles triangle of 120 degrees or the symmetry in the factors of an expression like $x^2 - a^2$. Internally, I always felt no particular "reason" for such liking to be on a different footing than having blue as a favorite color. There seemed to be more acceptance to the notion of having a favorite color than having favorite mathematical objects. I mostly kept this to myself.

I noted my reactions merely as observation while coming of age. I did not find others who discussed the emotional aspect of learning new mathematics, except for their frustration after failing to solve a difficult problem. For most I interacted with in high school days, mathematics was about conquering and meeting a challenge. Although I was successful at many of those challenges in school days, the disconnect between liking the blue color and liking parallel lines occupied noticeable space in my emotional world. Even now, most mathematics is taught in classrooms in a manner where emotions have no place – for understandable but often misplaced reasons.

One night, I remember vividly even today after three decades – It was late August, and it was raining heavily in Mumbai with the characteristic hypnotizing sound of rainfall on windowpanes. Everyone at home had slept, and I was up having liked some algebraic expressions. I dared to engage in exploring these emotional reactions. I sat down to write a "love letter" using concepts in mathematics I had learned at the time.

It was an experiment trying to see if I could invoke such character emotions with algebraic expressions as actors. I seemed to have the emotional reactions capable of invoking such feelings, out of what I had seen on the board a few times by then - at least to myself. I still remember the central theme of that letter, although unfortunately, I do not have the original letter. The idea that took center stage that night was that of appealing to my soulmate (not having met one) that we were capable of canceling each other's odds and merge into one free flow of 'even powers' for the rest of our incarnations in a supposedly infinite number of births that were yet to come. The lines on the paper were -

$$\frac{1}{1-x} = 1 + x + x^2 + x^3 + x^4 \dots \infty; |x| < 1$$

$$\frac{1}{1+x} = 1 - x + x^2 - x^3 + x^4 \dots \infty; |x| < 1$$

$$\frac{1}{(1-x^2)} = \frac{1}{2}\left[\frac{1}{1-x} + \frac{1}{1+x}\right]$$
$$= 1 + 0 + x^2 + 0 + x^4 + 0 + \cdots; |x| < 1$$

What I was writing that night made sense to me. To be sure, I checked it the next day, and I could still connect very well to those emotions. Of course, the next day and later, I was also aware that for many, this would not make any sense, and they would be quick to dispense this off as a crazy teenage thought. The letter that I wrote was in my mother tongue (Marathi), and I dispensed it off as well, thinking of it as something of a "child's play" and "teenage madness." The concept lingered in my head for years later, about a little more than two decades to be honest.

In these decades, I went through the engineering curriculum, took an excursion from the engineering curriculum to stay at home and study mathematics on my own, joined the prestigious school of mathematics at Tata Institute of Fundamental Research (T.I.F.R) for graduate studies in pure mathematics and returned to engineering for graduate studies at Brown University. After completing my doctoral degree, I became a practicing engineering professional with academic involvement as an adjunct professor and a private advisor. All along this journey, in all my academic involvement, I was aware that the letter, its emotional impact, and the concept of simultaneously experiencing mathematics and emotions never left me. I was aware of all my emotions through the learning process, particularly whenever I engaged in a mathematical query.

The first time I actively engaged in this "experiment in poetry" was when I published my first poetry book in my mother tongue – सामन ("Salmon"). As a section in that book, I published an experiment that I called "mathematical poems" (गणिती काव्य), which had most poems in Marathi and a few examples translated into English. The book was self-published with limited distribution, but I received good reviews from the readers. Quite a few expressed that they wished they could give the book to others they knew as a gift, particularly to share the mathematical poems. Unfortunately, the mathematical poems were mostly in Marathi, which limited the distribution further.

I took this as an opportunity to continue my inner journey of riding through emotions associated with mathematical concepts and engaged in a task I had not imagined - I started writing mathematical poems in English. Though English is not my first language, I found that the poems flowed when I engaged with my emotions and mathematics (although, in some instances, the intensity of expression was lost in translation). However, the result received positive responses from people to whom I presented the English version, and the present book is a result of that encouragement and goodwill from my well-wishers who conveyed their enjoyment.

In "Abstract Intersections," I have poems ranging from elementary concepts in mathematics such as points, lines, and simultaneous equations to some of the concepts from advanced mathematics based on topics in algebra, analysis, and topology. The idea is to draw parallels between some celebrated theorems and concepts in mathematics and life-experiences. In some poems, mathematical concepts form the backdrop in a metaphorical sense, and for some others, mathematical objects are the characters in the poem. For each poem, I have provided some mathematical context and some comments on emotional inspiration.

The mathematical context is mostly from how I learned or internalized the subject matter rather than stating mathematical facts like in a textbook. I have pointed to some external references where the interested reader can get more formal exposure to the subject matter. In some instances, of course, I am just reporting mathematical facts in providing mathematical context. Emotional inspiration has been somewhat difficult to write. Most of the emotional content is in the poem, and translating that loses the poetry. However, quite a few early presentations of the poems were appreciated more when I spoke to the emotional inspiration. Suggestions from the pilot readers were to have both sections for each poem. These section presentations' mannerism is not uniform for all poems because that is what felt appropriate to me as I wrote it. The reader familiar with the mathematical content and one who can connect to the emotions and parallels drawn, of course, have the option not to read those sections!

I hope you enjoy this unique literary experiment and cherish this unusual poetic journey.

- Kedar Hardikar,
  Santa Clara, CA, USA

♦

Content

♦

Singularity

Never did I realize that a singularity was near,
Every time I experienced this inner fear

Every encounter with a starred problem was demeaning,
But instead, it was an opportunity to question the meaning.

It wasn't about exceeding the expectation,
Neither was it a reason for frustration

Stripped bare was my ability to reason
To use it as a means to escape the prison

The naked truth was here to stare
Shaken was my "self" awakened and aware

The power of rationality is intertwined
With my desires "to be"
It lies in seeing without passion "If A then B."

♠

Singularity
Mathematical context:

Some mathematics books and instructors like to mark some exercises/problems as "starred" problems, indicating the problem's difficulty. For instance, a "double starred" problem (**) would suggest that you should expect some serious effort needed to solve it! My personal favorites were a set of starred problems from "Topics in Algebra" by I. N. Herstein, miscellaneous exercises in the classic "Higher Algebra" by Bernard and Child, and problems in the books "Challenging Mathematical Problems with Elementary Solutions, vol I and vol II" by A. M. Yaglom and I. M. Yaglom. This poem expresses facets of the emotional journey involved in solving such problems.

Usually, solving a starred problem is associated with a sense of pride for the mathematics student. However, for some of those who don't succeed at these challenging problems, their experience may be plagued with fear and questioning of self-worth in the sense of lacking the capability, unable to succeed in the competition with others, and not belonging to the "elite" club of "starred problem solvers." What was done by the author or instructor to help the student self-assessment be more effective has, in this case, an unfortunate side effect of the student categorizing himself/herself into a certain category based on the success rate at these problems and approaching the next starred problem with that prejudice.

The reference to the poem's singularity is with the mathematical notion of "singularity of a given function." One of the simplest examples of a singularity is the point $x = 0$ for the function $(x) = 1/x$. Here due to the inversion of x (i.e., taking reciprocal), the function "blows up." In this sense, singularity can be thought of as associated with "inversion."

Figure 1 illustrates the singularity in $\frac{1}{x}$. Figure 2 shows the inversion of the plane in a unit circle with a transformation $(r, \theta) \rightarrow \left(\frac{1}{r}, \theta\right)$ applied and the singularity of the function $f(r) = \frac{1}{r}$ at the origin.

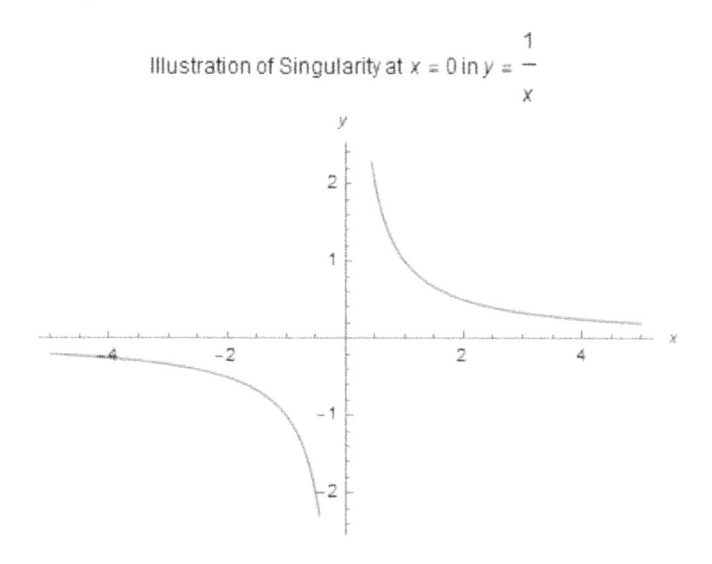

Figure 1. Graph of f(x)=1/x illustrating singularity at x=0

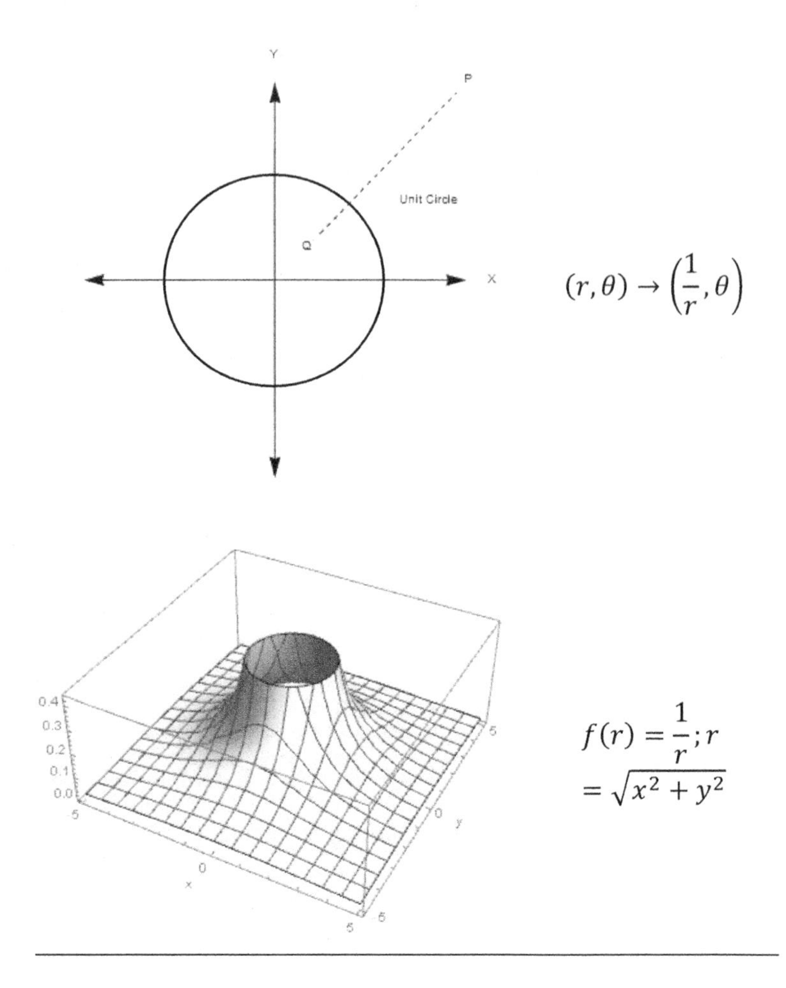

Figure 2. Transformation $(r,\theta) \rightarrow \left(\frac{1}{r},\theta\right)$ results in P and Q being images of each other illustrating "inversion" in unit circle with a singularity at (0,0).

Emotional Inspiration:

The poem draws upon the parallel between the inversion leading to singularity and the inversion of emotional experience perspectives with challenging problems. The inversion alluded to in the poem is the inversion of perspective from that of fear associated with the level of difficulty of the starred problem and the external image of self to see it as an opportunity where growth and redefinition of personality occur regardless of the outcome, in the internal world of self. I hope to convey the notion that was once conveyed to me by one of my most influential teachers – "Difficult problems should not come in the way of your education."

Often, when faced with such situations, what has helped me is going back to basics, disconnecting from the emotional turmoil associated with failure, and going again at the problem one more time with rational exploration and being open to the idea that you may not succeed.

♦

One

Just about when counting was fun
With a question, my pride was simply undone
“How do you define what you really meant...by ‘one’?”

My forehead was indeed wet
On my palms, I found some sweat
That this needed a strange set
Whose element in turn …was an empty set!

♠

One
Mathematical Context:

It is indeed an entertaining and simultaneously disturbing experience to question some fundamental notions we take for granted. One such question you can engage in is to try and "define" what we mean by "one" or what we mean by "zero." The requirement is that it should be a logically complete formal definition without pointing to physical objects. I must admit that I had not engaged in such a query till my exposure to "pure mathematics." Regular science and engineering curriculum was meant to crunch numbers and then look at physical objects to build some things. It did not provide such luxury. Nevertheless, when met with the question, it was not a matter of "luxury". Rather, it was a void that needed attention.

For example, one may say "the first whole number" is defined as "one." However, there is some incompleteness to this definition when you examine its logical completeness in the sense of it being a pure thought. At this stage of the query, "whole numbers" are not defined. For instance, one may ask what rule dictates that the number 2.5 does not belong to this set of "whole numbers"? The idea is to "define" the concept, which we associate with the abstraction that we call "one" when we refer to things such as "one marble," "one paper," "one pen," etc. At this stage of the query, the notion of "numbers" itself is in question, so using "first whole number" as a definition is somewhat odd and inadequate. Once you reach a stage in your query where you start questioning "what is zero?" or "what is one?" you quickly realize that we seem to have nothing to start with. Well, if you have nothing to start with, then we start with nothing! However, the questioning won't stop till we say: 'nothing' exists! The typical set-theoretic formulation will then start with an axiom –

Axiom (Empty set axiom): There is a set containing no members. In mathematical symbols –

$$\exists A \text{ such that } \forall x, x \notin A$$

Read as "There exists an A such that for all x, x does not belong to A."

We *call* this set an empty set. As a student, I have been guilty of not paying attention to the phrase "we call" in the prior statement – implying that "empty set" is a label and notion that resides in our perception, not otherwise. That label is a handle for whatever that internal notion is.

One of the most intriguing definitions of "one" is the set theoretic one that start from this axiom of an empty set. We can define an empty set $\phi = \{\}$ where our notion of "nothingness" is formalized. We have our intuitive notion of "size," which is encompassed in what we call "cardinality" in mathematics. If you now define a set $\psi = \{\phi\}$ whose only subsets are the empty set and itself, the cardinality of this set ψ is defined to be one. The interested reader should check graduate texts in mathematics that start with set-theoretic foundations for further details on this approach.

♦

Rational and Irrational

Numbers on the line
Stay in two categories fine
Rational and irrational
Seem to fill up the line

'Divide' says rational
And 'infinite' says irrational
When it is time to find your roots
You have got to give up the rationale

When you fight to set all square
You come across the one that's rare ($x^2 = -1$)
You cannot find the answer
And that is not unfair

Your foundation is shaken
And you are then awakened
The world view is broken
When granted things are taken

You are not really discrete
To let your perception complete
You need to free your mind
And let your ego deplete

Numbers on the line
Can make you see the divine
It is only when you transcend
That your soul will truly shine.

♠

Rational and Irrational Mathematical Context:

We consider numbers on the line to be of two types – at least in the elementary introduction, rational and irrational. Rational numbers are the numbers which can be expressed as $\frac{p}{q}$ where p and q are integers, e.g., ½, 1/3, 4/5, etc. Irrational numbers are the numbers that cannot be expressed in this form. Irrational numbers such as π can only be understood as a limiting value of a sequence of rational numbers (expressed as decimals, for example) or 'infinite decimals' for short. For example, the following sequence "tends to $\sqrt{2}$".

$$1, 1.4, 1.414, 1.4142, \ldots$$

When we look at the number line, it may appear that the number system should be complete with rational and irrational numbers. This belief holds until we come across an equation such as $x^2 = -1$, which we want to solve. At this point, I am going to take a much longer pause and detour because what I describe in the following passages is not the perspective that I saw in my formal education. I met others who had also not seen things in this way till they studied advanced mathematics. I believe that there is no reason for this to wait until exposure to advanced mathematics.

A simple review of the number system shows that at every stage of development of the number system, "new numbers" have been introduced to enable "solving some equations," which otherwise would be considered "not solvable." In the conventional curriculum, this is not how the number system is introduced.

Below is a brief outline of the evolution of the number system viewed from this lens, *not* meant to depict historical development accurately. If you are not interested in these details, you may skip to the statement of the fundamental theorem of algebra below.

a. Introducing negative integers–

- Addition: "10 objects in addition to 20 objects results in 30 objects total" => 10+20 = 30
- Subtraction: "10 objects removed from 20 objects results in 10 objects total" => 20-10=10
- In this view, equation 20-x=10 is solvable since you want to find out how many objects need to be removed from 20 so that the total remaining objects are 10?
- However, following this, the equation x+1=0 is "not solvable." It doesn't make sense to ask, "how many objects do I add to 1 to have nothing?". To enable "solving this equation," we need to *change the definition of addition and subtraction*. One such option is provided by defining them as movements on the number line. We can then reconcile these "new numbers" - the negative integers.

b. Introducing rational numbers–

- In the number system consisting of integers only, equations such as 2x-1=0 are not solvable since "there is no number which if you first double and then subtract one will give you zero." The idea of dividing two pieces of bread among three people does not fit in this world.

- The solution to such equations is enabled by introducing rational numbers or fractions defined as subdivisions of segments on the number line.

c. Introducing real numbers –

- Even when you introduce rational numbers, there are equations with rational coefficients which cannot be solved in a meaningful way e.g. $x^2 - 2 = 0$. A careful examination of this equation reveals a point on the number line, which is not a "fraction p/q with p and q as integers." You need special construction to make sense of these numbers. An example of construction for "solution of $x^2 - 2 = 0$, which we *denote* as $\sqrt{2}$ " is given below (figure 3).
- It might seem that all the points on the number line represent locations where some "polynomials" (curves defined with polynomials in x with rational coefficients) intersect the x-axis. If you collect all representable roots of polynomials, then will it "fill-up" the whole number line? Surprisingly, the answer is "No"! There are numbers such as π which cannot be represented as "roots of a polynomial." These are called transcendental numbers. When all these numbers- positive and negative rational numbers and irrational numbers, including transcendental numbers are collected, the number line is "filled."
- Are there still polynomials with real coefficients such that their solution does not make sense or does not exist? The answer is yes!

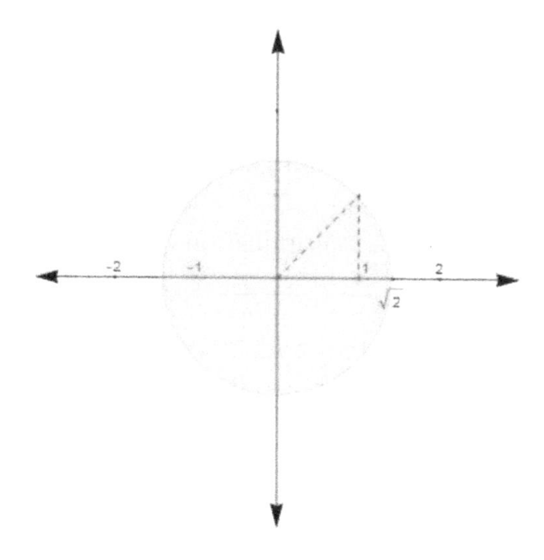

Figure 3. Special construction needed to identify $\sqrt{2}$ on the number line

d. Introducing complex numbers –

Even after defining Real numbers, we are faced with the fact that the polynomial $x^2 + 1 = 0$, which has its coefficients as real numbers, does not have a solution in real number system. To enhance this number system, we introduce "new numbers" called complex numbers. It is natural to feel the discomfort in introducing $\sqrt{-1}$. The following passages hopefully provide a different perspective.

A complex number is an ordered pair of real numbers z= (x,y) with rules and operations defined below :

i. $z_1 = (x_1, y_1) and\ z_2 = (x_2, y_2)$are equal if and only if (iff) $x_1 = x_2\ and\ y_1 = y_2$
ii. 0 = (0,0)

iii. $z_1 + z_2 = (x_1 + x_2, y_1 + y_2)$; $-z = (-x, -y)$ defines the "inverse" of addition giving z+(-z) = 0 which can be conveniently "represented" as z-z=0.
iv. Product is defined using the rule $z_1 z_2 = (x_1 x_2 - y_1 y_2, x_1 y_2 + x_2 y_1)$
v. The inverse of a multiplication operation is defined using $z^{-1} = \left(\frac{x}{x^2+y^2}, -\frac{y}{x^2+y^2}\right) with\ x^2 + y^2 \neq 0$. It is easy to verify that $z * z^{-1} = 1$ using the product rule in (iv). Hence it may be *denoted* as $z^{-1} = 1/z$

Note that the above "newly introduced" number system is essentially a "two-dimensional" number system and can be *represented* on a plane for convenience (figure 4). However, in principle, we could not introduce any graphical representation of these numbers and proceed with their definition purely as a pair of real numbers. One can think of numbers $(\alpha, 0)$ as corresponding to real numbers introduced earlier. Also note that the usual addition, subtraction, multiplication, division operations on real numbers are consistent with the above definitions for this new number system. Now, in particular, we see that

$$z = (0,1)$$

$$by\ above\ multiplication\ rule\ satisfies$$

$$the\ polynomial\ equation$$

$$z^2 + 1 = 0$$

We would like to think of real numbers as forming a subset of these complex numbers. We would like to continue using them following our usual formalism of manipulations with algebraic operations. *Hence it is convenient* to define a *symbol* $i = (0,1)$ as a root of $z^2 + 1 = 0$, thereby leading to $i^2 = -1$. All complex numbers can now be represented as $z = x + iy; x = Re(z), y = Im(z)$ where x and y are real numbers and $Re(z)$ *and* $Im(z)$ are *called* real and imaginary parts of complex number z. It is easy to verify that multiplication by $i = (0,1)$ can be represented as "counter-clockwise rotation by 90 degrees about origin" on the complex plane. Hence correspondingly, multiplication by i^2 represents rotation by 180 degrees, which is the same as multiplication by -1.

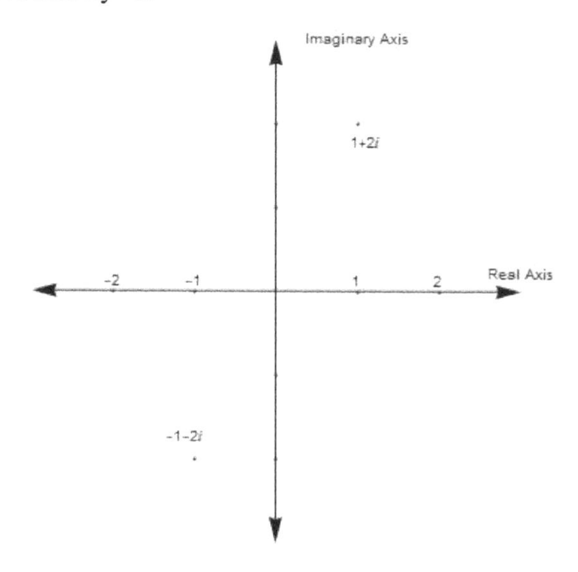

Figure 4. Representation of complex numbers in a plane.

<u>Polynomials</u>: Polynomials are complex-valued functions of a complex variable

$$p(z) = a_0 z^n + a_1 z^{n-1} + \cdots + a_{n-1} z^{n-1} + a_n$$

$$Where\ n\ is\ non-negative\ integer$$

$$and\ a_0, a_1, \ldots, a_n\ are\ complex\ numbers.$$

The highest power of z with non − zero coefficient is called the degree of the polynomial. A root of polynomial p (zero of p) is a complex number r such that $p(r) = 0$.

Fundamental Theorem of Algebra: If p is a polynomial such that degree p ≥ 1, p has at least one root (in complex numbers).

This is a celebrated theorem and a rather remarkable result. Not every polynomial with real coefficients has a root in real numbers. It follows from above that if p is a polynomial of degree n ≥ 1 with leading coefficient $a_0 \neq 0$ then p has exactly n roots, i.e., $p(z) = a_0(z - r_1)(z - r_2)(z - r_3) \dots (z - r_n)$

Emotional Inspiration

I will start by bringing your attention to a fact that was missed in my school curriculum. Due to the need for more freedom in formal calculations, the use of negative and rational numbers was brought about. The hesitation in the introduction of such numbers is understandable. I wish we were told this when in school. Leopold Kronecker, a famous mathematician, once said, "God created natural numbers. Everything else is man's creation". Only at the end of middle ages did mathematicians begin to lose their uneasiness in using these concepts, which did not have the same intuitive concrete character as natural numbers. It was around the middle of the nineteenth century that mathematicians accepted that the logical and philosophical basis for operating in extended number domains is formalistic because definitions create the extensions. Although the definitions are free, they will be rendered worthless unless they are extended so that prior rules are consistent with the extensions introduced.

The last statement of the fundamental theorem of algebra is many times referred to as a statement of "completeness" of complex numbers in the sense that any polynomial in the 'world of complex numbers' will have its root in the 'world of complex numbers' and you do not need to go beyond.

The poem draws upon the parallels between how you need to break the barriers and redefine the notions to make new equations solvable in mathematics and how you evolve in your journey of life, gradually freeing your mind of the previously held world-view. In doing so, we have to reconcile the prior view with the new enhanced perspective. A poetic way to look at this evolution is that you will not see the true completeness unless you transcend the 'rational' and 'irrational.'

♦

Negative Signs Matter

Once in my dream, I met the depressed “negative one.”
In the darkest of her hours, she was told
Think positive for success or your life will be done

Struck by (this) oppression
Beaten and broken
Her family and community were forced
To hold the sign of regression as their token

None of them could be called a hero
They needed to climb
Even to reach a milestone
That was called the zero

Tears rolled down her eyes
As she described the zero as a mere “ugly round.”
With righteous anger, she said,
“We all are mere numbers, why the hell are we labeled as
‘Below the ground’?”

Her entire life, to her, seemed dispensed
For the preference of positive roots of equations
Negative ones
Were many times expensed

With protests of sorts, the dawn had arrived
When with criticality of a quadratic
The concept of "i" was derived

The privilege of positives
Now this derivation could shatter
With supremacy and completeness of the complex numbers
Everyone came to know that the negative signs matter.

♠

Negative Signs Matter
Mathematical Context:

The mathematical context for this poem is the same as the context for "Rational and Irrational." There is a reference made to discarding the negative roots of equations in the poem. This is quite common in solving practical problems that can lead to a polynomial equation. Only the positive ones are taken when all the solutions are found since the negative solutions are not practical.

One interesting example of this where discarding the negative values can make you miss some interesting and fun insight is presented below –

Consider the problem of finding the points of intersection of the hyperbola $\frac{x^2}{a^2} - \frac{y^2}{b^2} = 1$ with coordinate axes. To find points of intersection of the curve with the x-axis, we set y=0 and get $x^2 = a^2 => x = \pm a$. Hence points of intersection are $(a, 0) and\ (-a, 0)$. This is easily seen in plotting the hyperbola (figure 5). However, following the same procedure for $x = 0$ leads to $y^2 = -b^2$ and we may discard this case since there are no real numbers that will satisfy this relation. The answer to this equation in complex numbers is $y = \pm ib$ where $i = \sqrt{-1}$ is the imaginary unit. Is there a significance to this answer or a relevant geometric insight that we would miss if we discarded the second case?

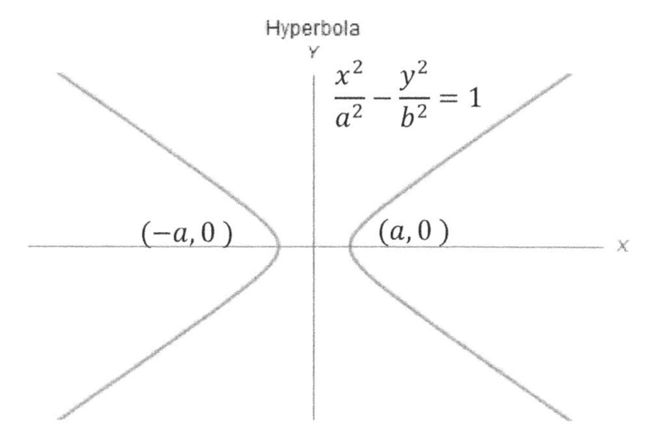

Figure 5. Hyperbola in-plane representation and as a conic section.

To understand the significance, let us "construct" the hyperbola as a section of a cone. Consider a cone with a semi-angle of α placed with its tip at the origin and axis aligned with the x-axis (see figure 6). A cut perpendicular to the X-axis of this cone is a circle in $Y - Z$ plane with a radius $x \tan \alpha$. Hence, it is easy to see that the equation of this conical surface is $y^2 + z^2 = (x \tan \alpha)^2$. If this cone is cut along the plane $z = h$, the resulting equation is $y^2 + h^2 = x^2 \tan^2 \alpha$ or equivalently, $\frac{x^2}{(h^2/\tan^2 \alpha)} - \frac{y^2}{h^2} = 1$, which is a hyperbola in standard form. Now it is clear that the solution to $x = 0$, in this case, is $y = \pm ih$ and corresponds to the height h "outside" of the plane of hyperbola where the conical surface touches the Y-axis! As a student, when I did this calculation, I have wondered how the "i" somehow imagined of an intersection outside of the world where the hyperbola lived. I will leave you to enjoy the wonder, but since that night, I decided for myself to discard the notion that is calling $i = \sqrt{-1}$ as an "imaginary" number was a misnomer (which is how mathematics instructors explain it many times). I enjoy living with the mystery – calling it imaginary is more fun, so why not?

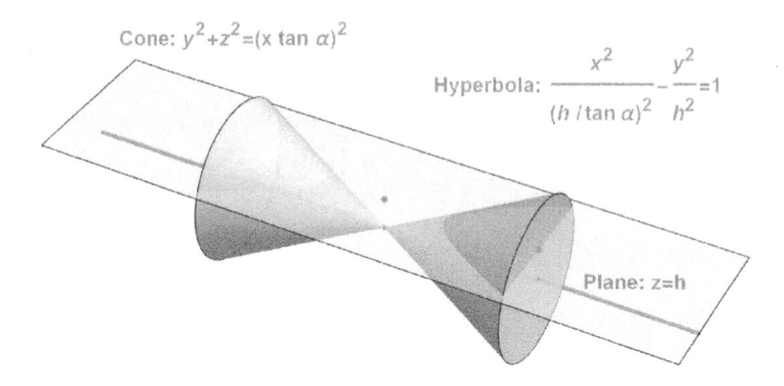

Figure 6. Hyperbola as section of a cone with semi-angle α and an illustration of seeking the intersection of a hyperbola with the Y-axis in the plane of the hyperbola.

Emotional Inspiration

I would have preferred to leave it mostly to poetic expression; however, I will make some select comments, since some individuals may miss some facets of this poem. The poem is written with the backdrop of emotions typically experienced by under-represented segments of society. These could be groups facing bias due to gender, racial/ethnic background, religion, or sexual orientation. An example relevant to this book would be women in mathematics or science.

As an exercise, I would suggest the reader re-read the poem changing the gender representing "-1" and examining your emotional reaction. If there is none, it is great news, but on the other hand, if changing the gender impacted your internal reaction to the poem, it may be worthwhile to re-read the poem with this lens applied to other under-represented segments of society. The example above where I solved for what $\pm ih$ represents provoked the thought that even in inanimate objects, such as numbers, a deep-rooted bias (like that with negative numbers) prevents us from gaining incredibly important insights and "seeing the light" as revealed by complex numbers. Let alone treating humans with any bias!

♦

Modular Arithmetic

On an afternoon walk
My wristwatch and I had a strange little talk

The shadow beneath my feet
Had grown a little smaller
The dirt on my shoes reminded of that kid
Who had lived in squalor

What mattered was the bread
The waters ahead to tread
To what had past, no attachment, no thread

As he grew, his vision grew
With knowledge and wisdom
The skills acquired were new

All along, the indefinite progression of natural numbers
Had resonated within
The day, the week, the month and next…
It was as if he followed a 'map built-in.'

But with growth came cycles of desires
And patterns to be found
Obscured in the numbers was a secret
For that afternoon to expound

With sadness and sorrow
He had gone round and round
The indefinite marching of numbers
Conflicted with his intuition, I found!

Satiating desires had always bred a few more
Marching of the numbers resonated within no more
The illusion of milestones had melted under the sun
Every vision was plagued with this inherent limitation

The hours of my watch wrapped around the noon
Cycles were assigned to the Sun and the Moon
Decades after decades and generations anew
Experiences retraced like congruent numbers
With prime moduli a few

Failures, the loss, and the grief
Are no more traumatic,
Now the cycles of life seem like
A grand display of modular arithmetic!

♠

Modular Arithmetic
Mathematical Context:

I will start by introducing in simple terms what is "modular arithmetic." We all are used to referring time with 12-hour cycles or 24-hour cycles. For example, if we ask ourselves what time it would be 3 hours from ten in the morning, the answer is one in the afternoon. A 24-hour-cycle calculation will say 3 hours from 10:00 is 13:00. The idea of reporting time after subtraction of 12 hours from 13:00 and using 1:00 pm as our answer is a concept formalized in what is called modular arithmetic. In the language of mathematics, the calculations on the clock represent a "modulo 12 calculation". More formally, in mathematics, the following statement is made about integers a, b, c

$$a \equiv b \, mod \, c$$

to mean that when a is divided by c, the remainder is b

(The symbol $a \equiv b \, mod \, c$ is read as "a is congruent to b, modulo c")

An alternate statement is the following -

$a \equiv b \, mod \, c$ implies that numbers can be written as

$a = m \times c + b$ for some integer m.

The following statements will make sense using the above definition and provide you a perspective on how the calculation works

$$11 \equiv 1 \, mod \, 10$$

$$-1 \equiv 9 \, mod \, 10$$

$$11 + (-1) \equiv 9 + 1 \equiv 0 \; mod \; 10$$

$$-3 \equiv 3 \; mod \; 6$$

$$11^2 \equiv (2)^2 \equiv (-1)^2 \equiv 1 \; mod \; 3$$

When modulus c is a prime number, several interesting and powerful implications can be derived. Modular arithmetic has many interesting applications. One place where simple and elegant applications can be found is in deriving divisibility rules for integers. As an example, let $a_n a_{n-1} a_{n-2} \dots a_0$ represent a $n + 1$ digit number where $0 \leq a_i \leq 9$ for each i. Now evaluate the number modulo 11.

$$a_n \times 10^n + a_{n-1} \times 10^{n-1} + \cdots + a_1 \times 10 + a_0 \equiv a_n(-1)^n + a_{n-1}(-1)^{n-1} + \cdots + a_2 - a_1 + a_0 \; mod \; 11$$

The RHS will be zero if the original number is divisible by 11. However, the RHS will be zero if and only if the sum of "odd place digits" is equal to the "sum of even place digits." This is precisely the rule for divisibility by 11!

Emotional Inspiration

The poem seeks to draw parallels between the cycles involved in modular arithmetic and emotional experience cycles as we evolve through our life experiences.

On an afternoon walk
My wristwatch and I had a strange little talk

The shadow beneath my feet
Had grown a little smaller
The dirt on my shoes reminded of that kid
Who had lived in squalor

What mattered was the bread
The waters ahead to tread
To what had past, no attachment, no thread

This segment is a glimpse of the past flashed in a moment of contemplation by the narrator. The context is that of a poor kid who grew up in a family where it was difficult to make ends meet. In such extremes, one is often focused on the basics. It is also a situation in which one is often thankful when those basic needs are met. When those desires are met, a natural thirst for growth and a sense of growth come with more desires to fulfill.

As he grew, his vision grew
With knowledge and wisdom
The skills acquired were new

All along, the indefinite progression of natural numbers
Had resonated within
The day, the week, the month and next...
It was as if he followed a 'map built-in.'

Such growth at an early age is often associated with our sense of indefinite progression, just as how natural numbers progress indefinitely. Our sense of mortality is very weak, despite the knowledge that we all will die one day. The false sense of immortality is referred to as the "map built-in" and is mapped to the indefinite progression of natural numbers.

But with growth came cycles of desires
And patterns to be found
Obscured in the numbers was a secret
For that afternoon to expound

With sadness and sorrow
He had gone round and round
The indefinite marching of numbers
Conflicted with his intuition, I found!

Satiating desires had always bred a few more
Marching of the numbers resonated within no more
The illusion of milestones had melted under the sun
Every vision was plagued with this inherent limitation

As we grow to satisfy our desires, we find ourselves moving through cycles of emotions that seem to repeat. Fulfilling one set of desires often breeds new desires. The cycles of happiness and sorrow repeat through these experiences. Although we sense this as 'growth,' the illusion that leads us through the cycles of emotions escapes our comprehension. This leads to an internal conflict that we recognize but find hard to resolve. The "milestones" that once felt like significant accomplishments and worth achieving start to lose their luster after getting to those in our progression. The narrator recognizes it as a direct conflict like that in the indefinite natural numbers progression vs. the same numbers rearranged in modular arithmetic in cycles.

The hours of my watch wrapped around the noon
Cycles were assigned to the Sun and the Moon
Decades after decades and generations anew
Experiences retraced like congruent numbers
With prime moduli a few

Failures, the loss, and the grief
Are no more traumatic,
Now the cycles of life seem like
A grand display of modular arithmetic!

These stanzas refer to our assignment of cycles to our sense of the day and night. While this assignment is consistent with our daily experience on earth, we often fail to be cognizant that it is valid only relative to where we are. Only when we transcend our sense of mortality and realize the whole of life experience as a mere cycle that one can hope to achieve liberation.

♦

The Point

A raindrop had not splashed after falling from the sky
The sand at the beach made me wonder why?

The breeze at the shore had dried up my sweat
Awakening me to some mysteries,
That challenge my mindset!

Weight and breadth and length and height
None of them matter, said someone not in my sight

Alone on the beach, I looked around for the monster
The sand, those drops, and the breeze
Had one vastly different answer!

The notion of the continuum had plagued my view
Millions and billions of points .... was the reality, not new!

"A dot on the paper" is how you describe it
"Impressions inside" was the right way to see it

My core was now shaken since my world view was broken
Those images on the paper were nothing but a mere token!

Everything around is points adjoint
And the origin of the universe resides in The Point!

♠

The Point
Mathematical Context:

The geometric concept of a point is not trivial to “define.” One candidate statement that may be considered as a “definition” is that point is a geometric entity indicating location in space. It does not have length, width, height, or volume (dimensions), but it exists. In modern mathematics, the point is defined as an element of a set called space.

Emotional Inspiration

These definitions point us to examine the philosophical aspect of the definitions and dealing with a fundamental entity that cannot be defined in terms of previously defined objects. In particular, the above definitions certainly indicate that the notion of point has to do with the impression we carry in our mind of an entity that does not have physical dimensions or attributes, but we accept its existence axiomatically. Our notion of the continuum (empty space) is essentially that of considering everything around as points adjoint.

♦

The lines

Theorems and proofs and lemmas and riders
In the army of geometry, I was looking for insiders

Barely had I learned to speak to 'the point.'
The teacher then said,
A line is nothing …. but points adjoint!

With the passing of the day, the class had worsened
The burden of the proof was now placed on the innocent

"Measure straight along the ground," claimed the Geometry
While it seemed to me that this claim was outright bigotry.

Along the very ground, my mind had drawn it right
It traveled around the earth
And returned to the original site!

The hoax of a straight line was caught in plain sight
The teacher and her torture were about to lose this fight

I stood by my guard and asked her a simple question
I said, "Before wasting time, let us clear up our perception

The burden of the proof should lie with the guilty
The notion of a straight line seems incredibly faulty

Draw it out straight, and here is what I have found
Travelling along such a thing,
You will certainly lose your ground!

Enjoy your flight in space,
And here is where you lose this race
Since everything is moving in space, first tell me ...,
Where is your base?"

That night, I had won and seemingly conquered the lines
He who bends the world to his will
Shall be the one who shines!

Years later, with a mind serene and calm
It dawned upon me
That they had caused some measurable harm
All along quietly sitting .... on the face of my palm!

♠

The Lines
Mathematical Context

The geometric concept of a straight line is subjected to some scrutiny in this poem. If we examine our notion of a straight line, we quickly realize that the line cannot be defined with reference to the ground. If we do so, we will travel along the round earth and will lose the notion of the line being "straight." This suggests that for the line to be "straight," one would have to start from the ground and leave the ground going into space to keep it "straight." However, once you are in space, the "reference point" matters. Since everything is moving in space, it is not clear what our notion of the line being "straight" really is! In physics, the "straight line" in space is the path followed by light.

Emotional Inspiration

No additional comments. I will leave it to the original poetic expression.

♦

The Circle

I remember that night with showers and thunder
While getting in shape,
A circle had fallen in love with its center!

Lightning in the sky had struck with some zest
For the meeting of these soulmates was indeed,
An incredible quest

Round and round the circle had wandered
The crossing of the radius was a problem it pondered

A crisis of identity had struck at the core
It wanted to know about its origin some more

An element of doubt was corroding the purity
Was 'many circles for one center' a sign of promiscuity?

"Why would the center love me?" It wondered at last
"Is this my destiny?" - the thought had now crossed.

Well, I had some choices in my incarnations
Parabola, Hyperbola, and Ellipse
Were certainly my options

Ellipsis of sorts had paused its thoughts
For being an ellipse,
Two foci would bring two lovers ...it thought!

Being a parabola sounded almost like a tragedy
For part of itself would have to be sent to infinity!

After all, it thought, we were born as conic sections
In our birth were written several imperfections!

Showers and thunder had now soaked to its core
Connection of soulmates needed radii no more

The night of enlightenment had brought harmony of hearts
Both of them decided to give up their parts

The barrier of radius, the circle, had thrown
To embrace its circle, the center had grown
Losing one's identity was the path love had shown.

♠

The Circle
Mathematical Context:

The only mathematical context that needs to be provided is for the following stanzas.

Well, I had some choices in my incarnations
Parabola, Hyperbola, and Ellipse
Were certainly my options

Ellipsis of sorts had paused its thoughts
For being an ellipse,
Two foci would bring two lovers ...it thought!

Being a parabola sounded almost like a tragedy
For part of itself would have to be sent to infinity!
After all, it thought, we were born as conic sections
In our birth were written several imperfections!

The references made here are for the mathematical fact that the circle, parabola, ellipse, and hyperbola are the curves that are obtained by sectioning cones as shown in figure 7 below:

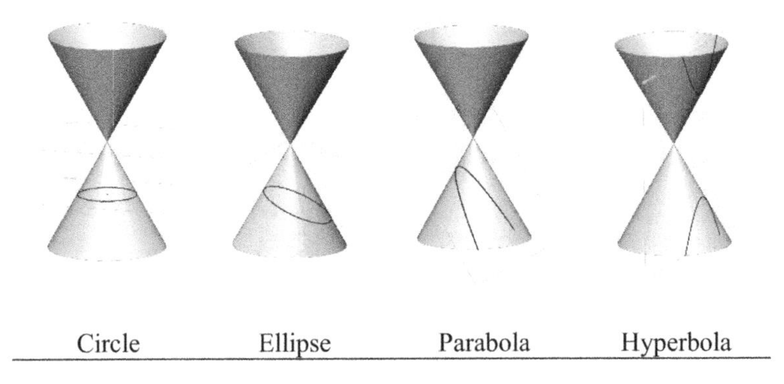

Figure 7. Illustrations of conic Sections

Interestingly, circle, parabola, and ellipse can be thought of in terms of transformations from one curve to the other. For example, an ellipse can be thought of as a circle projected at an angle. An ellipse is typically characterized by two points called foci, which have the property that a sum of distances of any point on the ellipse from the foci is constant, as shown in figure 8. A circle is a special case of ellipse where the two foci merge into one point that we refer to as the circle's center.

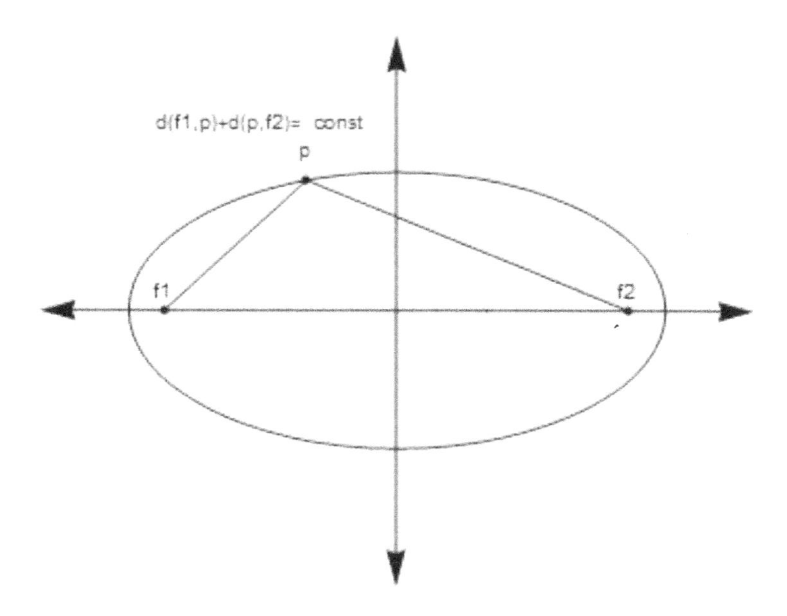

Figure 8. Ellipse with two foci and the property related to distance from two foci.

Similarly, somewhat less obvious is a transformation where an ellipse can be transformed into a parabola when part of it is "sent to infinity." For those familiar with the mathematical representations of these curves, the following calculation could be entertaining.

Let us start with an ellipse with semi-major and semi-minor axes to be a *and* b respectively, and distance between two foci to be 2c. When the ellipse is placed to have one vertex at the origin, the equation of the ellipse is $\frac{(x-a)^2}{a^2}+\frac{y^2}{b^2}=1$. We can rearrange the equation as

$$y^2 = b^2\left[1-\frac{(x-a)^2}{a^2}\right] = b^2\left[2\left(\frac{x}{a}\right)-\left(\frac{x}{a}\right)^2\right]$$
$$\approx \frac{2b^2}{a}x \; for \; large \; a \; \left(or \; small \frac{x}{a}\right)$$

However, this means that in this transformation, the ellipse tends to become like a parabola as the other vertex is "sent to infinity"! One other property of these curves suggests a similar relation. It is known that a ray originating from one focus of an ellipse, when reflected in the boundary of the ellipse, will pass through the second focus. For a parabola, a ray originating at its focus when reflected in the boundary travels parallel to the axis – as if "searching for its other focus at infinity." These are shown in figure 9 below –

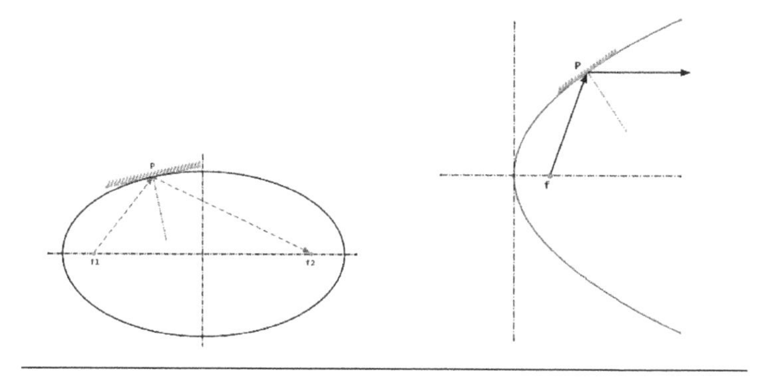

Figure 9. Reflection property of Ellipse and Parabola.

The sense described above in which to transform from an ellipse to a parabola, the other focus is "sent to infinity" is what is referred to in the poem as -

> *Being a parabola sounded almost like a tragedy*
> *For part of myself would have to be sent to infinity!*

Emotional Inspiration

No additional comments. I will leave it to the original poetic expression.

♦

Simultaneous Equations

Her clear blue eyes
Had just about blinked
When dimples on her cheeks
Had gently kinked.

The world of equations
Had opened her heart
Equations bivariate (she thought)
"Was the new math....or art?"

Chromosomes in the body
Had different incarnations
Meeting of the mates
Needed solving of equations

Give and take apart (she said)
But be gentle with one's heart
Renouncing the powers
Is good enough of a start.

Equations on the paper
Sought merging of domains
Mimicking that in love
Is now all that remains!

Simultaneous equations
Gave her an incredible insight
For harmony of hearts
Think 'compassion' rather than 'fight'!

♠

Simultaneous Equations Mathematical Context:

The only mathematical context that needs to be provided here is for the lines –

Equations on the paper
Sought merging of domains
Mimicking that in love
Is now all that remains!

Consider solving simultaneous equations $\{y - x = 4, y + x = 6\}$. The solution can be represented graphically, as in figure 10. Each equation represents a line (1-D domain), and the solution to the simultaneous equations is the place where the two domains merge.

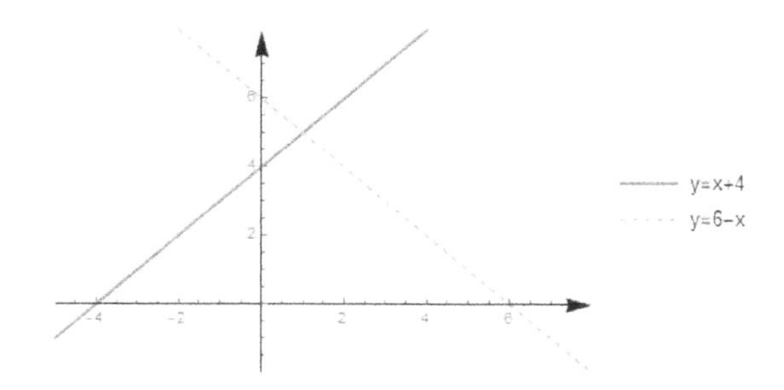

Figure 10. Graphical representation of the solution to simultaneous equations

Emotional Inspiration

Often in solving simultaneous equations, variables such as $x \text{ and } y$ obey certain relations (e.g., in above case $y - x = 4, y + x = 6$) that define separate domains. In simple cases, the relation is linear, but it can be a complicated relation. To solve this, these relations obeyed by the two variables have to be rearranged with some "give and take" on the two sides of the equality to look for "common ground." For instance, adding the two equations would give $2y = 10$, and subtracting the two would give $-2x = -2$, thereby enabling the solution $x = 1 \; and \; y = 5$ where the two domains will merge. Each has its own set of characteristics in a loving relation between two individuals (that define their domain). In a healthy relation, we have to have some "give and take" and actively seek common ground through compassion rather than focusing on the differences.

♦

The Theorem of Pythagoras

Grads and Radians had waited their turn
Stars at the pole suggested “360” in turn

Its number of divisors were sweeter than 2Pi
The metric for the angles was won in a close tie!

Affairs and love triangles had troubled many of hearts
Mature was Mr. 90 that kept upright, its parts!

Joining of its ends was one diagonal’s dream
Measuring that length needed a talent supreme!

Marriage of the squares, only diagonals could dare
Pythagoras said, you better give this one a good stare!

In this orthogonal setting, were hiding many cute couples
Out of them were born the Pythagorean triples!

These matches made in heaven caused exponents to fight
Dying Fermat said - My friends, only squares got this right!

♠

The Theorem of Pythagoras
Mathematical Context:

We are used to a degree as a measure for angles in geometry. However, it is natural to ask why a measure, such as 90 degrees, is assigned to a right angle. Why not 100? Is there something special, about 360 degrees? Why not some multiple of hundred like 400? Turns out that this has been attempted in some developments. There are some interesting measures of angles in geometry. Two of the angle measures other than degrees are grads and radians. Grad (or gradian) is an angle measure that corresponds to $1/400^{th}$ of a full circle. Radian is an angle measure defined by arc length divided by the radius where full circle corresponds to 2π radians. While radian is a preferred measure for the angle in higher mathematics, grads are not used as frequently. Degrees are often used in practical calculations involving angles. It raises the question - what could be the advantage of using the geometry of angles without being "metricked"? Three of those advantages are as below –

- If interested in astronomy, the Earth going around the sun in 365 days would suggest 365 as representing the full circle. However, it would lead to division issues, and using a closer approximation 360 would make more sense.
- It is expected that divisions of an angle would be often needed in geometry. Any number of divisions of the circle would work as a measure. However, 360 has many divisors making it easy to assign simpler values to smaller angles. The divisors of 360 are – $\{1,2,3,4,5,6,8,9,10,12,15,18,20,24,30,36,40,45,60,72,90,120,180,360\}$.
- Using a measure such as 400 for full circle would force us to use 200 as a measure for straight line, and a simple

symmetric figure such as an equilateral triangle would have an angle measure $200/3$, very inconvenient to use!

Pythagoras theorem is well known to anyone having taken elementary school mathematics. Pythagorean triples are set of integers $\{a, b, c\}$ *that satisfy* $a^2 + b^2 = c^2$ e.g., 3,4,5. It is known that there are infinitely many Pythagorean triples. The last line of the poem refers to what is known as Fermat's Last theorem. This is a famous conjecture first proposed by French mathematician Pierre de Fermat in 1637. It had to do with seeking a set of integers a, b, c which satisfy a relation $a^n + b^n = c^n$ where $n > 2$. He stated that it was impossible to find such integers for exponent $n > 2$. The conjecture was written in his notes and was discovered some 30 years after his death (without proof). The first proof of this "theorem" was given in 1995, i.e., almost after three centuries, and this was considered one of the most difficult problems in mathematics. Research intended to prove/disprove this "theorem" has driven several significant developments in modern mathematics.

♦

Compound Interest

Interest on the interest
Had earned some ridiculous blame
Romans called it usury
An unfair kind of game

Concealed in the compounding
Was the Euler's constant 'e.'
Through the "force of interest."
It was revealed by Bernouilli

In the mathematics of my mortgage
With a student's derivation astray
Balancing of the interests (in the equation)
Made my emotions sway

One side of the account
Compounds my obligations
Reciprocity of interest
Dictates balancing of relations!

♠

Compound Interest
Mathematical Context:

Compound interest is introduced quite early in school education, and most of us are familiar with the concept. However, it is worth noting that when it was introduced, it was not received very well. Charging interest over interest was considered by Romans to be an unfair means to extract money from the borrower and was once condemned by Roman law. It took a long time for compound interest to become the norm in borrowing.

When we calculate monthly payments against a loan, there is a typical mistake that a student makes, which I have personally made when doing the calculation as a student. To illustrate this, let us consider a simple question –

Question: If you borrow loan amount P for a period n (e.g., 36 months for a typical car loan) with an interest rate r (consider this monthly). What is the monthly payment you need to make?

Below is a common mistake (which I have also made as a student) that gives you the wrong answer:

$$Total\ amount\ you\ owe = P(1+r)^n$$

$$Monthly\ payment = M = \frac{P(1+r)^n}{n}$$

Right Answer: The correct calculation is as follows –

When you make a monthly payment M back to the lender, the lender also makes interest income on those payments (presumably at the same rate as that of the loan). For example, the first monthly payment M grows to $M(1+r)^{n-1}$

over the total period of the loan, the second monthly payment grows to $M(1+r)^{n-2}$ and so on. Hence, the correct monthly payment is that which balances the two. In other words –

$$P(1+r)^n = M[(1+r)^{n-1} + (1+r)^{n-2} + \cdots + (1+r)^0]$$

This simplifies to

$$Monthly\ Payment = M = \frac{rP(1+r)^n}{(1+r)^n - 1}$$

Note that for sufficiently small r, the two answers are approximately equal. Historical developments involving compound interest suggest that one of the significant constants (Euler's constant e) was derived by Jacob Bernoulli in 1683 while studying a question related to compound interest. The question that prompted Bernoulli's investigation was to find what happens to the growth function $\left(1+\frac{1}{n}\right)^n$ where interest is compounded over smaller and smaller intervals, i.e., what happens to the limit $\lim_{n\to\infty}\left(1+\frac{1}{n}\right)^n$? He noticed that it approaches a constant (referred to as Force of interest), which we now know to be $'e'$. Euler is credited with using this constant as a base for natural logarithms. The constant $'e'$ is of enormous importance in mathematics.

Emotional Inspiration

There is a subtle emotional bias associated with the mistake involved in the wrong answer presented above and the correction needed. The first approach merely accounts for your obligation. The second approach demands balancing your obligation against what the other entity derives from your payments, thereby balancing both sides' interests! Of course, the last two lines are intentionally written to connect to interpersonal relations while being true in the mathematical context for the compound interest calculation.

♦

Renunciation of Powers

$$\frac{1}{1-x} = 1 + x + x^2 + x^3 + \cdots \infty; |x| < 1$$

Geometric progression
When taken to infinity
Shows me away
To march to eternity

I can relate to x's
As my incarnations
Perceived are those powers
They're the mind's own creations!

Smaller than the divine
And different from 'The one.'
If that is who I am
I won't feel enlightened

Renounce all your powers
And listen to the sages
You will see the divine
When you break free from cages.

♠

Renunciation of Powers
Mathematical Context:

A sequence of numbers $b_0, b_1, b_2, \dots, b_n$ such that the ratio of two consecutive numbers is a constant r is known as Geometric Progression i.e. $\frac{b_1}{b_0} = \frac{b_2}{b_1} = \cdots = \frac{b_n}{b_{n-1}} = r$. Such a sequence can be represented using initial term a and common ratio r as a, ar, ar^2, ar^3 .... It can be shown that the sum of first n terms of a geometric progression is given by

$$S_n = a + ar + ar^2 + \cdots + ar^{n-1} = \frac{a(1 - r^n)}{1 - r}$$

When the common ratio is less than 1 i.e. $|r| < 1$, it can be shown that the above series, when taken to infinity, has a finite limit i.e.

$$\lim_{n \to \infty} S_n = \frac{a}{1 - r}$$

It follows that

$$1 + x + x^2 + \cdots \infty = \frac{1}{1 - x}; |x| < 1$$

This result has some interesting consequences. For instance, imagine that a ball dropped on a wooden floor bounces to half of the height from which it dropped when it hit the ground. This ratio (1/2 in this case) is dictated by a property called the coefficient of restitution. If you drop this ball from 1m, the total distance it will travel before settling on the floor will be -

$$1 + 2 \times \frac{1}{2} + 2 \times \frac{1}{4} + 2 \times \frac{1}{8} + \cdots \infty$$

$$= 1 + 2 \times \left(\frac{1}{2} + \frac{1}{4} + \cdots \infty\right) = 3m$$

Emotional Inspiration

The poem draws parallels between the unexpected consequence of having a finite limit to the infinite sum in geometric progression to the concept of cycles of life and reincarnation. When you examine the sum $1 + x + x^2 + \cdots \infty$ there is no apparent reason why this sum will have a closed-form representation. The different powers of the variable x obtained as $x, x^2, x^3, \ldots$, are metaphorically seen like different incarnations of the soul through several births. Further, the poem also points to a poetic way of looking at the closed-form answer $\frac{1}{1-x}$ $with\ |x| < 1$. The infinite sum representation is valid only as long as:

$$|x|\ is\ smaller\ and\ different\ from\ one.$$

One other subtle feature of the result is that on the right-hand-side we have "all the powers" of x including the first term as x^0, while the left-hand-side does not have powers of x. When $|x| < 1$, higher powers make the terms smaller. The parallel being drawn here is the spiritual perspective that we suffer cycles of birth and death if we separate ourselves from the divine and exist as smaller than the divine. The usual notion that you grow when you have higher powers is challenged in this perspective. If you do not have an element of divine perspective in you, you may grow smaller in pursuit of higher and more powers. It is only when we seek to be one with the divine that we can achieve nirvana.

♦

Taylor Series

$$f(t + \Delta t) = f(t) + \Delta t\, f'(t) + \frac{\Delta t^2}{2!} f''(t) + \cdots \infty$$

Taylor wrote a series
That will seal all your worries
For an insight to the future
Lies in dreams today you nurture

The key to knowing future
Is to know today's change
It marches on infinitely
And so, it looks strange

You continue soul-searching
As you look at all your speeds
What a bright future needs,
Are many of good deeds!

♠

Taylor Series
Mathematical Context:

Taylor Series in mathematics is an infinite series where the value of a function in the neighborhood of a given point $e.g. f(x + \Delta x)$ Is expressed using derivatives and their values at the given point $e.g. f(x), f'(x), f"(x)$, etc. as below

$$f(x + \Delta x) = f(x) + \Delta x\, f'(x) + \frac{\Delta x^2}{2!} f"(x) + \cdots \infty$$

Brook Taylor introduced Taylor's series in 1715. For most common functions, the function's value and the sum of the infinite series agree in the neighborhood. When only finitely many terms on the right-hand side of the above relation are used, this provides a polynomial approximation to the function in the neighborhood of point $'x'$.

Emotional Inspiration

When written in time-variable $'t'$, the Taylor series provides a statement that appears strange and raises philosophical questions. The equation is as below -

$$f(t + \Delta t) = f(t) + \Delta t\, f'(t) + \frac{\Delta t^2}{2!} f"(t) + \cdots \infty$$

When written as above, the left-hand side of the equation is a value of the function in the "future," whereas the right-hand side has all the terms evaluated "at present." An example of approximating the values of the function $f(t) = e^t$ "in the future," knowing "present" derivatives (at t=0) is shown below in figure 11.

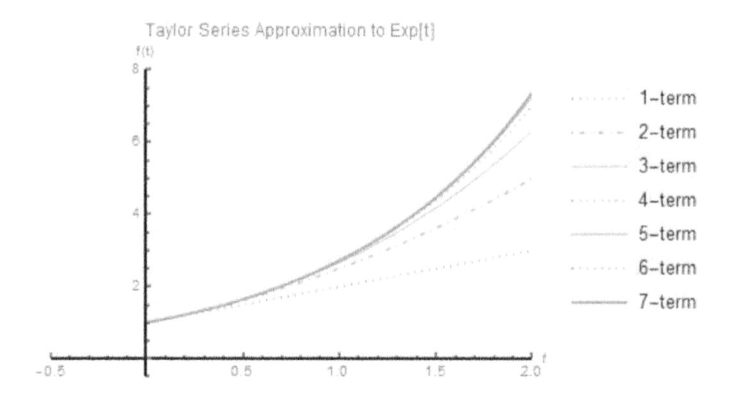

Figure 11. Taylor Series approximation and improvement with more terms

So, the essence of the Taylor series is that it provides a way to "predict" the values in the future if we know all the "speeds" (derivatives used in the most general sense) in the present. In this sense, the insight into the future lies in knowing today's change and speeds. The poem attempts to draw the parallel between this mathematical relation and the philosophy of Karma where today's good deeds will dictate your future.

♦

Fourier Series

Any continuous function on $[-\pi, \pi]$, can be approximated by series consisting of sines and cosines as-

$$f(x) \approx \frac{a_0}{2} + \sum_{n=1}^{\infty} a_n \cos nx + b_n \sin nx$$

$$a_0 = \frac{1}{2\pi}\int_{-\pi}^{\pi} f(x)dx\,;\ a_n = \frac{1}{\pi}\int_{-\pi}^{\pi} f(x)\cos nx\,dx\,;\, b_n = \frac{1}{\pi}\int_{-\pi}^{\pi} f(x)\sin nx\ dx$$

In the mystery of the heat
You won't really see it
Any shape curve or function
Has the same things in it

You need a different eye
Or this insight will pass by
All things look so different
But they are one when you go high

When you truly stand tall
And listen to your heart's call
What the Fourier series shows
Is 'The one' that is inside us all!

♠

Fourier Series
Mathematical Context:

Fourier Series in mathematics was discovered by Jean Baptiste Joseph Fourier, a French mathematician, born in Auxerre, France. He established the partial differential equations governing heat conduction and solved them using the infinite series, now called the Fourier Series. Fourier series provides an approximation of periodic functions by an infinite series consisting of sines and cosines. An example of approximating a square wave function using Fourier series is shown below (figure 12). As the number of terms increase, the approximation improves (except at points of a discontinuity).

$$f(x) = \frac{4}{\pi}\left(\sin x + \frac{\sin 3x}{3} + \frac{\sin 5x}{5} + \frac{\sin 7x}{7} + \cdots \infty\right)$$

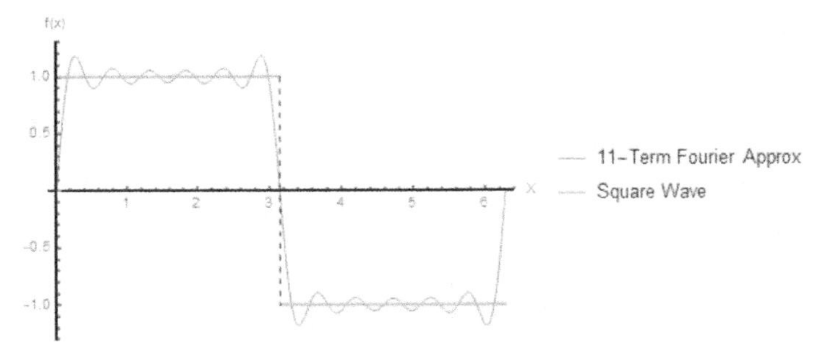

Figure 12. Fourier Series Approximation of Square Wave with 11-term Fourier Series

Emotional Inspiration

What Fourier series shows is the ability to represent various shapes using the same basic elements – the waves (sines and cosines). The poem appeals to the commonality among us all which we may label as "The one inside us all", in the sense that each of us is a mere different representation of the same elements.

♦

Differentiation under the Integral Sign

Differentiation under the integral
Was it a crime of thoughts?
Adamant of integrals claimed
It was intercourse of sorts!

The privilege of the constants
Was abused by the derivative
Challenging integrals fought
Their case with this narrative

You were hiding a parameter
Inside the integrand
New techniques had to be brought
Claimed the first defendant

Integrals decided
To defend their pristine fort
The case was then moved
To proceed in Lebesgue's court

Rieman's old sum
Had failed to defend the case
Dominated convergence
Had shaken integral's base

Sets of measure zero
Had cast functions in a class
Limiting of sequences
Had obtained the required pass!

With limits on their side
Derivatives followed
Parameters in integrands
Were elegantly swallowed

The case was then closed
With Lebesgue, integrals were hosed
Analysts then rejoiced
And in textbooks, this technique was posed!

♠

Differentiation under the Integral Sign
Mathematical Context:

Differentiation under the integral sign is typically introduced to students of calculus as a technique to solve some difficult integration problems. The idea is to express the integral $(say\ I)$ as a function of a parameter $(say\ p)$, which is different from the variable of integration $(say\ x)$. Expressing the integral as $I(x,p)$ allows you to use the derivative with respect to p on the integral and it can simplify the calculation as shown below.

Let us say we want to evaluate

$$I = \int_0^1 \frac{x^{\sqrt{2}} - 1}{\ln x} dx$$

This integral is not easy to evaluate by simple trials. We will now see how we can use differentiation under the integral sign. Instead of the exponent $\sqrt{2}$ let us replace it with a parameter p in the integration process.

$$I(p) = \int_0^1 \frac{x^p - 1}{\ln x} dx$$

Now, for the function $I(p)$, we can differentiate with respect to p on both sides

$$\frac{d}{dp} I(p) = \frac{\partial}{\partial p} \int_0^1 \frac{x^p - 1}{\ln x} dx$$

On the right-hand side, there is a derivative outside of the integral sign. These two, the differentiation and integration, are "opposite" operations. However, since the differential is with respect to parameter p, which is different from the variable of integration x, the derivative can be taken inside, i.e. under the integral sign. Of course, for this passing of the differentiation to the other side of the integral sign to be valid, certain conditions need to be met. For now, we will assume that the conditions are indeed met, and it can be done with legitimacy.

$$\frac{d}{dp}I(p) = \int_0^1 \frac{\frac{\partial}{\partial p}(x^p - 1)}{\ln x} dx$$

Noting that $\frac{\partial}{\partial p}(x^p - 1) = x^p \ln x$, it follows that

$$\frac{d}{dp}I(p) = \int_0^1 x^p dx = \left.\frac{x^{p+1}}{p+1}\right]_{x=0}^{x=1} = \frac{1}{p+1} => \frac{dI(p)}{dp} = \frac{1}{p+1}$$

The last relation can be easily integrated in p to give

$$I(p) = \ln(p+1) + C$$

The constant of integration C can be determined noting that at $p = 0$ the original integrand $(x^p - 1)/\ln x$ is zero and hence $I(p = 0) = 0 => C = 0$. Hence, $I(p) = \ln(p + 1)$ and we are done! The specific case of $p = \sqrt{2}$ gives $I = \ln(1 + \sqrt{2})$ as the final answer.

If you have tried the original integral by elementary means and failed, this technique appears like a little magic show in solving those difficult integrals. However, the most important question is – when is it valid to take the derivative inside the integral sign in the manner used in the above example? Can it always be done? While in many well-behaved functions it can be done, it turns out that this question can be rightfully answered with some advanced mathematical concepts. To explain these, we need to resort to what is called Lebesgue Integration (named after the French mathematician Henri Lebesgue) and Measure Theory. Following passages can be thought of as one of the simplest (in some sense oversimplified) and hopefully an entertaining introduction to the relevant concepts.

Elementary calculus deals primarily with two geometric problems – finding tangents to curves and finding areas of regions defined by curves. The first requires a limiting process called *differentiation* and the second also involves a limiting process which we call *integration*. When viewed as two geometric problems, there is no reason that the two would be related – but they are indeed intimately related! This fact by itself is fascinating! In elementary calculus, the area under the curve defined by function $f(x)$ bounded by interval $[a, b]$ is calculated by integration as a limit of the sum of areas of little strips obtained by subdividing the interval into smaller intervals Δx_k each centred at the point x_k. As the number n of subdivisions increase, the intervals Δx_k become smaller. See figure 13

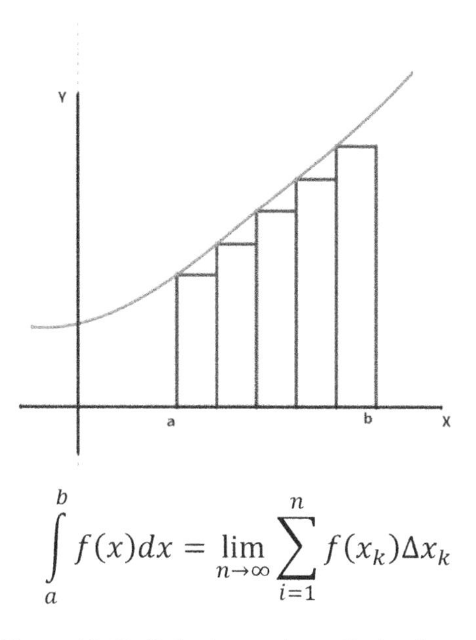

$$\int_a^b f(x)dx = \lim_{n\to\infty} \sum_{i=1}^{n} f(x_k)\Delta x_k$$

Figure 13. Definite integral as a limit of a sum.

If function $f(x)$ is sufficiently well behaved in $[a, b]$, e.g. continuous, we can hope that the above limit exists. This is roughly the concept of what is called Rieman Integration. Certain pathological functions will miserably fail to be integrable in this sense. We will construct one such example to motivate Lebesgue Integration and the concept of measurable sets.

Consider set S to be a subset of the interval [0,1]. An example would be $S_1 = \left\{x \middle| 0 \leq x \leq \frac{1}{2}\right\}$. Let us define a function which identifies whether a given x is in the set S_1 as in figure 14.

$$f_1(x) = \begin{cases} 1, & x \in S_1 \\ 0, & x \notin S_1 \end{cases}$$

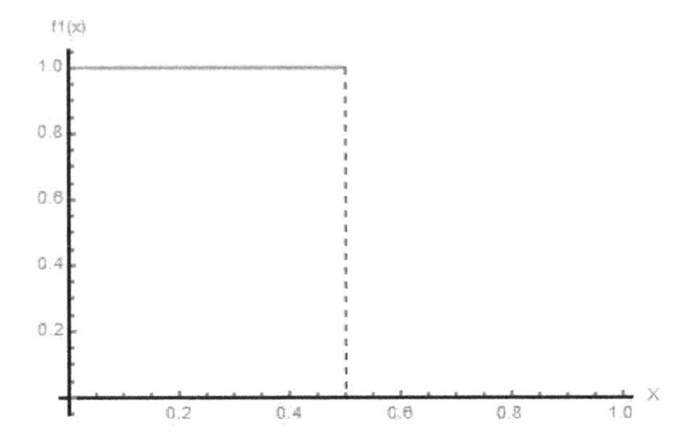

Figure 14. Representation of $f_1(x)$

Since this is a step function non-zero over $\left[0, \frac{1}{2}\right]$, it is quite easy to see that $\int_0^1 f_1(x)dx = \frac{1}{2}$. The value of the integral represents the "size" of set S_1. This seems like a simple technique to assign "size" to a given set. Now, consider another set whose size we would like to investigate – the set of rational numbers. So, we define -

$$g(x) = \begin{cases} 1, & x \textit{ is rational number} \\ 0, & x \textit{ is irrational number} \end{cases}$$

In this case, we will see that the integral $\int_0^1 g(x)dx$ defined as Rieman Integral will fail to exist because we can not meaningfully get through the limiting process for the sum involved. This raises the question "how much space out of the unit interval is occupied by rational numbers vs irrational numbers?" (e.g. is it half and a half?). When I first saw the answer to this question, I must admit that I lost sleep over this. The method used to answer this question is quite intriguing. Consider arranging all rational numbers in the following infinite table (s) –

	1	2	3	4	...	
1	1	2/1	3/1	4/1		
2	1/2	1	3/2	4/2		
3	1/3	2/3	1	4/3		
4	1/4	2/4	3/4	1		
5	1/5	2/5	3/5	4/5	1	
.	1/6	2/6	3/6	4/6	.	
.	.	.	.	.		
.	.	.	.	.	.	

(a)

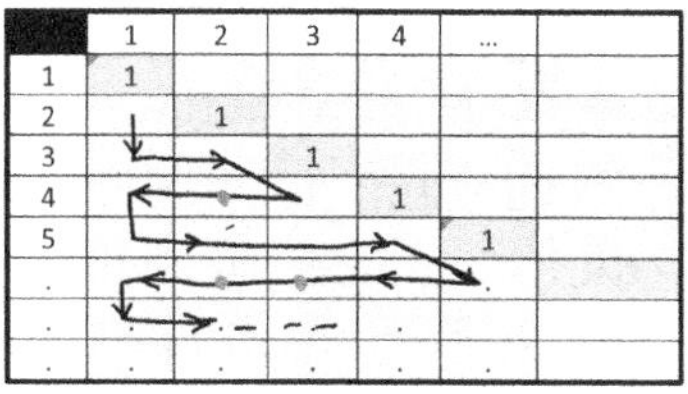

	1	2	3	4	...	
1	1					
2		1				
3			1			
4				1		
5					1	
.					.	
.	.			.		
.	.	.	.	.	.	

(b)

Figure 15. (a)Arrangement of rational numbers in [0,1] (b) method of "counting".

Figure 15 (a) shows a way to arrange all rational numbers in [0,1] in a way that they can be "counted" using the scheme in figure 15(b) as in first, second, third etc., skipping any when we encounter "repeats" (e.g. skip 2/4, 3/6, 2/6 ..marked by red dots). So, now *all* the rational numbers in [0,1] are arranged in the sequence $\{a_0, a_1, a_2 \ldots\}$. Now we go through a simple exercise of drawing a tiny open interval around each of those numbers with lengths $\left\{\frac{\epsilon}{2}, \frac{\epsilon}{2^2}, \frac{\epsilon}{2^3}, \ldots\right\}$ etc. In other words, the number a_0 is "covered" with an interval of length $\frac{\epsilon}{2}$, a_1 is covered with an interval of length $\frac{\epsilon}{4}$ etc. where ϵ is an arbitrary (small) number. Now we can ask the question – what is the total length of the segment needed to cover all the rational numbers in [0,1]? The answer is –

$$l = \frac{\epsilon}{2} + \frac{\epsilon}{2^2} + \frac{\epsilon}{2^3} + \cdots \infty = \epsilon \frac{\left(\frac{1}{2}\right)}{1 - \left(\frac{1}{2}\right)} = \epsilon$$

$$(using\ infinite\ geomertric\ series)$$

This means that to cover all the rational numbers in [0,1] the length of the segment needed is merely ϵ, which is arbitrarily small! Most of the line segment of [0,1] is then made up of irrational numbers although we know that the rational numbers can be found in any given sub-region of [0,1]!! In the language of Measure Theory, what we have demonstrated is that the set of rational numbers in [0,1] is a "set of measure zero" (vanishingly small size). What can be said about $g(x)$ in the language of Measure Theory is that " $g(x) = 0$ *almost everywhere in* [0,1]" since the subset where it is non zero is itself of measure zero. With this understanding, we can now provide a logically consistent answer to $\int_0^1 g(x)dx$ if it were to represent the "size".

$$\int_0^1 g(x)dx = \int_{set\ of\ measure\ zero} 1\, dx + \int_{set\ of\ measure\ one} 0\, dx = 0$$

This way of thinking about the integral using "measurable sets" and their "measure" (size) is the essence of Lebesgue Integration. It is in this setting that most satisfactory answer to the validity of differentiating under the integral sign can be provided. In essence, the question then boils down to the following. If $f_n(x)$ is a sequence of functions with certain convergence behavior "pointwise" in [0,1], i.e. at a given x we know the behavior of $\lim_{n\to\infty} f_n(x)$, when can we say that

$$\lim_{n\to\infty} \int f_n\, dx = \int \lim_{n\to\infty} f_n\, dx\ ?$$

Since differentiation is also a limiting process, once the condition for above exchange of limit and integral are established the relevant conditions for taking the derivative inside the integral (in the manner described in the earlier example) can be obtained. The relevant important theorem in this analysis is Lebesgue's Dominated Convergence Theorem which leads to the relevant conditions for legitimacy of differentiation under the integral sign. The interested reader can go through the details in a mathematical analysis graduate text such as “Mathematical Analysis, by Tom Apostol”.

Emotional Inspiration

I prefer to leave it to the original expression without additional comments.

♦

Measure Zero

On a Sunday evening with a cup of tea
Deconstructing my world
One moment at a time
It dawned upon me that
Toward my own "self."
I was about to commit a smooth crime

Rationality of Monday
Will consume me in a few hours (I thought)
I will wake up tomorrow and mindlessly say
To the day, "I am all yours."

I walk along an interval ...a continuum
Practicing my notion of empty space
Sprinkled along were such rationales...
Ignoring the residuum
That morphed this walk into an irrational race

The characteristic function
Of "my time" evolved
When with the characteristic function
Of such rationales it convolved

"There is plenty of room at the bottom."
Claimed one who I saw as my hero
He spoke of taking the atoms apart
With an insight into the continuum sublime and thorough

With a warm sip out of my cup
On the empty beach
A Lebesgue integral then shined
Better than the setting sun and the twilight
Like a wave splashing over to reach
My heart ran around to beseech
With my breath confined
I could not recall a thing as my week's highlight

An insight from the Lebesgue integral
I was then prepared to borrow
The empty space between and within atoms
Will dictate my understanding of the material for tomorrow
I then made up my mind to not live "my life" in
Densely spaced rational instances of measure zero!

♠

Measure Zero
Mathematical Context:

The mathematical context for the poem is the "sets of measure zero". This concept was introduced in the context of the previous poem - "Differentiation under the integral sign". The Lebesgue integral referred to in the poem is also the same as that referred to in the previous poem. For the sake of completion, I will mention the integral and its details with a slight modification.

A characteristic function $f_1(x)$ of a set S_1 is a function which identifies whether a given x is in the set S_1

$$f_1(x) = \begin{cases} 1, & x \in S_1 \\ 0, & x \notin S_1 \end{cases}$$

Thus, characteristic function $g(x)$ of the set of rational numbers Q would be defined as

$$g(x) = \begin{cases} 1, & x \textit{ is rational} \\ 0, & x \textit{ is irrational} \end{cases}$$

Note that the product $h(x) = f(x)g(x)$ will render $h(x)$ nonzero only at rational points, and everywhere else it will be zero even when $f(x)$ is nonzero everywhere. This process is what is referred to in the lines below (although convolution in mathematics is a slightly different product)–

The characteristic function of "my time" evolved
When with the characteristic function
Of such rationales it convolved

The function $g(x)$ defined over unit interval $[0,1]$ can not be integrated using conventional Riemann integral (integral as a limit of a sum) as discussed earlier. It is only when we invoke Lebesgue integral (discussed in the context of the previous poem) that the integral is meaningful and shown to be zero. It is worth noting that the set of rational numbers is "dense" in the interval [0,1] in the sense that in any arbitrarily small neighborhood around any point in [0,1] you will always find a rational number.

There is a separate reference to the quote – "There is plenty of room at the bottom". There was a famous lecture by physicist Richard Feynman at the annual American Physical Society meeting at Caltech on December 29, 1959. The title of the lecture was "There's Plenty of Room at the Bottom: An Invitation to Enter a New Field of Physics". In this lecture, Feynman considered the possibility of direct manipulation of matter at the atomic scale.

Emotional Inspiration

I prefer to comment less and leave it to the original expression. The poem is about scrutiny of how we spend time and what fraction of it is spent in activities that are meaningful to us vs activities to which we assign meaning by convention.

♦

A Branch Cut

Another decade has passed
As I logged it in my diary
I closed one, and a fresh one started
With a simple query

Some sorrow, some joy
And some lost kinship
Why do I feel some familiarity?
With this recent hardship?

There was a time
When all these daily logs were simple
The base was real,
Power unshaken and my mind nimble

Complexities of life
Had shown some unimaginable turns
And in my heart,
The residues of those decades left some burns

With every turn,
I had revisited some familiar barriers
My wisdom and lessons from the past,
I thought, were my warriors!

As decades turned,
I had gained some and lost some
The barriers to cross
Had also seemingly morphed some

A closer look and scrutiny
Had revealed some truth
My recent hardships –
I had also encountered their replica in my youth

Everything I experienced had revolved
Around me with my mind at the center
My core was the place where,
In life, some singularities could enter

Complex logarithms I taught for years
Had been telling me a story
Why didn't I see it earlier?
It now relieved my core having seen past the mystery

The cycles of barriers and hardships and their noise
I could now easily shut
The decades were not repeating but instead
Landed me on another high with a branch cut

Beautifully laid in my notes
Was the truth I had avoided to face
My emotions had mapped my decades
To sheets of the Rieman surface!

♠

A Branch Cut
Mathematical Context:

A branch cut is a concept encountered in Complex Analysis. I will attempt to take a short-cut to introduce the concept and its relevance without losing the entertaining part. In the mathematical context for the poem "Rational and Irrational" a framework for the introduction of complex numbers as an extension of the number system, we call "Real Numbers" was laid out. As we extend the formalism, the new definitions are in principle "free" to be whatever we want. However, they are useful only when they maintain consistency with the prior definitions which supposedly have a smaller scope. When we extend the number system from real numbers to now include complex numbers, some of the operations such as addition, multiplication, inverse, etc., have simple extensions which were discussed earlier. However, some other operations are not so trivial to extend. I will recall a question related to having real numbers in "power function" – what do we mean by the number $2^{\sqrt{2}}$? ($2^3\ is\ 2 \times 2 \times 2$, 3 times. What is $2^{\sqrt{2}}$?) It turns out that to "define" the number a^b for any <u>real</u> numbers a, b (e.g. $a = \pi, b = \sqrt{2}$) we need to resort to the definition of an exponential function e^x as an infinite series -

$$y = e^x = 1 + x + \frac{x^2}{2!} + \frac{x^3}{3!} + \cdots \infty$$

The reason this can be taken as "definition" of e^x is that the infinite series can be shown to converge and give a well-defined result for all real values x. Also, it can be shown that the inverse of this function is defined unambiguously for positive values y and can be denoted as $x = \ln y\ for\ y > 0$. Hence, $2^{\sqrt{2}}$ can be *defined* to be $e^{\sqrt{2}\ln 2}$, where $\ln 2$ is defined by the inverse of the function e^x.

With the above consideration, a noble question to ask is – how can we extend the two functions, namely, e^x and $\ln(x)$ to complex number system? Wouldn't it be nice to have a similar definition for $z_1^{z_2} = e^{z_2 \ln z_1}$?

It turns out that using the conditions for convergence of a power series in a complex variable, it can be shown that the series $e^z = 1 + z + \frac{z^2}{2!} + .. \infty$ converges everywhere in the complex plane. By substitution and simplification, we are now able to *define trigonometric functions* of a complex variable as –

$$\cos z = 1 - \frac{z^2}{2!} + \frac{z^4}{4!} + \cdots + \frac{(-1)^n z^{2n}}{(2n)!} + \cdots$$

$$\sin z = 1 - \frac{z^3}{3!} + \frac{z^5}{5!} + \cdots + \frac{(-1)^n z^{2n+1}}{(2n+1)!} + \cdots$$

Also, it is seen that, $e^{i\theta} = \cos\theta + i\sin\theta$ (Euler's formula) for any *real* variable θ. One interesting aspect that I had missed the first time, as a student, is that our geometric connection to defining sine and cosine using right triangles with phrases such as "sine is opposite side divided by hypotenuse" is nowhere in the picture in these definitions because now sine and cosine are "defined" as power series. The Euler's formula is a consequence of the exponential function definition and how the substitution works out. In this approach "it so happens" that the power series definitions coincide with the definition of sines and cosines as the ratio of sides of right triangles, showing that the new definition extends previous notions learned in elementary trigonometry just as the new definition of complex numbers extended our previous notion of number operations as we knew it in the real number system.

Now, to define logarithm in the complex plane, we need to investigate the inverse of the function e^z. This is essentially defined by the effort to seek solutions to the equation $e^z = w$ and denote it as $z = \ln w$, where $w\ is\ a\ given\ complex\ number$. We know that e^z is not zero for any z, and hence logarithm is not defined for $w = 0$. When $w \neq 0$, we must have $|w| = |e^z|$. When $z = x + iy\ with\ x, y\ as\ real\ numbers$ we must have by use of Euler's formula –

$$|w| = |e^z| = |e^{x+iy}| = |e^x||e^{iy}| = |e^x||\cos y + i \sin y|$$
$$= |e^x|\sqrt{\cos^2 y + \sin^2 y} = |e^x|$$

This also leads us to have a relation between the imaginary part of z and argument of w to be $y = \arg w + 2\pi k$ for some integer k. However, this means that the definition of $\ln w$ gives a "multi-valued function" since k can be any of the integers. To define the logarithm uniquely, we need to restrict the associated argument (angle) range to $0 \leq \theta < 2\pi$ or $-\pi \leq \theta < \pi$ (as some examples). This restriction means that we have effectively introduced a "cut" in the plane to define the possible angles. One representation of such a cut corresponding to $-\pi \leq \theta < \pi$ is shown in figure 16.

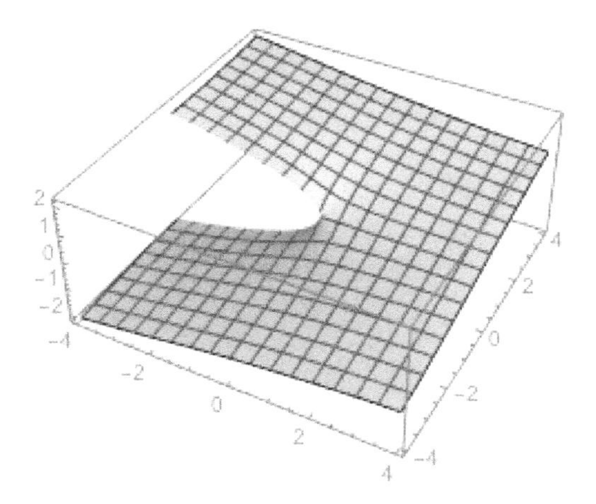

Figure 16. Illustration of a branch cut along the negative x-axis. The z-coordinate and shift in the image are for illustration purpose only, and the point at the origin is excluded.

This concept is extended further by what is called a "Riemann Surface" where, with every cycle of "rotation of the angle by $2\,\pi$" if we consider such sheets glued together along the "cut", then logarithm can be defined uniquely on this multi-sheet structure where, as $'k'$ changes in $2\pi k$ we travel on different sheets of the Rieman surface rather than going around on the same plane. An illustration of this concept of the Riemann surface is shown in figure 17.

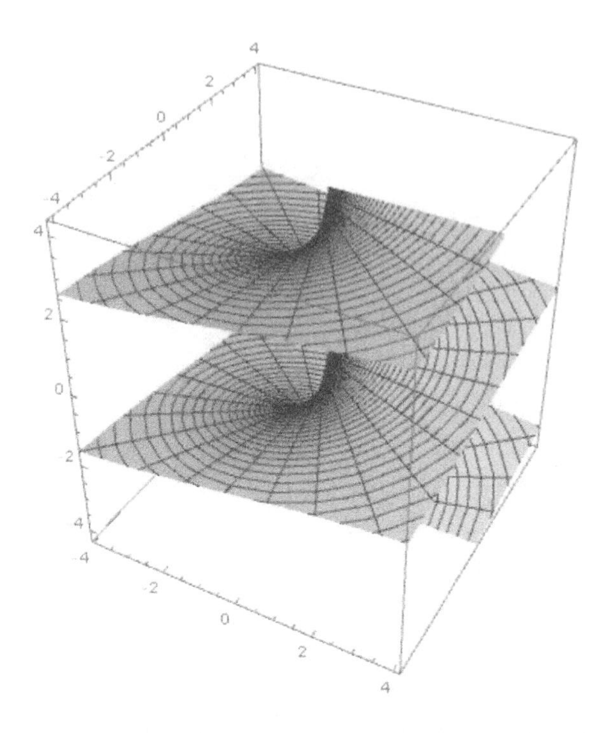

Figure 17. Illustration of Riemann Surface for $(-2\pi, 2\pi)$ and associated sheets. The z-shift used in the figure is for illustration purpose only, and the point at the origin is excluded.

Emotional Inspiration

The poem starts in the form of introspection and reconciliation of events in life over a few decades and the recognition that there are patterns to our emotional journey, which are probably dependent on our experiences. They also depend on how we processed our experiences while facets of our personality developed in formative years.

Another decade has passed
As I logged it in my diary
I closed one, and a fresh one started
With a simple query

Some sorrow, some joy
And some lost kinship
Why do I feel some familiarity?
With this recent hardship?

Usually, such intense introspection is forced upon us when we experience events that we perceive as "life-changing". Often, they are events which bring some hardship. The likelihood that we engage in introspection and reconciliation at the time of happy events is, unfortunately, lower, although, exceptions may exist. Such reconciliation often leads us to a quest involving rediscovery of our core.

There was a time
When all these daily logs were simple
The base was real,
Power unshaken and my mind nimble

Complexities of life
Had shown some unimaginable turns
And in my heart,
The residues of those decades left some burns

The second half of the poem is focused on reconciliation. After the initial query, we engage in the objective assessment of the experiences with a broader and often a new perspective.

With every turn,
I had revisited some familiar barriers
My wisdom and lessons from the past,
I thought, were my warriors!

As decades turned,
I had gained some and lost some
The barriers to cross
Had also seemingly morphed some

A closer look and scrutiny
Had revealed some truth
My recent hardships –
I had also encountered their replica in my youth

There is a hint here that this process is similar to that involved in the inspection of function definitions in real variables and extending them to complex variables which often requires redefinition with a broader perspective. A parallel has been drawn between the crossing of the axes as the argument involved in logarithm changes with 2πk in complex logarithm and overcoming barriers in life experiences which bear some semblance to past experiences or even may be influenced by past experiences. The reference to singularity later is to the singular behavior at origin for logarithm paralleled with how critical our core is in how we process our life experiences. In redefining logarithms in the complex plane as single-valued function, expanding the domain to Riemann surface is involved. This is a paradigm shift which leads us to realize that we are never really re-tracing the "angles" but in fact, climbing to different sheets of the Riemann surface. Reconciliation of life experiences has been mapped to a similar evolution where our experiences may go through cycles, but with each cycle, we evolve. We don't really retrace the cycles of experiences exactly although some similarity to past experiences may exist.

Everything I experienced had revolved
Around me with my mind at the center
My core was the place where,
In life, some singularities could enter

Complex logarithms I taught for years
Had been telling me a story
Why didn't I see it earlier?
It now relieved my core having seen past the mystery

The cycles of barriers and hardships and their noise
I could now easily shut
The decades were not repeating but instead
Landed me on another high with a branch cut

Beautifully laid in my notes
Was the truth I had avoided to face
My emotions had mapped my decades
To sheets of the Rieman surface!

♦

Residue Theorem

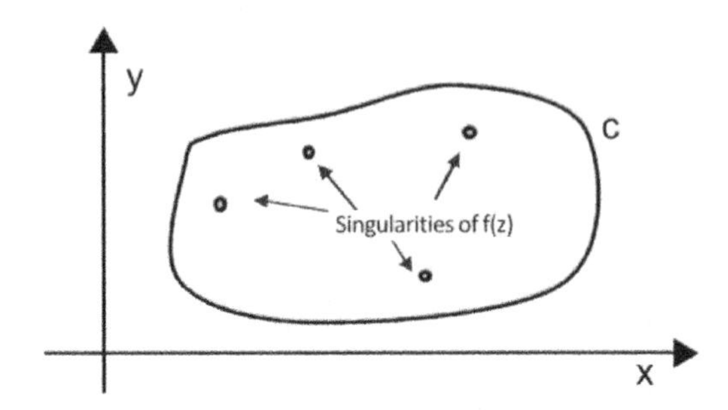

If C is a simple closed curve in the complex plane, the contour integral of a function $f(z)$ along C is given by

$$\int_C f(z)dz = 2\pi i \sum Res(f, a)$$

Where $Res(f, a)$ denotes residue of f at $z = a$, the summation is to be carried out over all singular points $z = a$ in the interior of (enclosed by) the curve C.

Round and round you have wandered
Looking for a treasure
Why didn't you just see it
'Inside' was the pleasure!

If you integrate your life
On the paths that you have taken
When things went all wrong
That is when you were shaken

Residues of your actions
Are the legacies you leave behind
If you have shared a lot of love
You will live on in people's mind.

♠

Residue Theorem
Mathematical Context:

Residue theorem is a theorem introduced in complex analysis. The object of attention is the contour integral, i.e. integrals along a path in the complex plane.

A simple closed curve C in complex plane $\mathbb{C}$ is a curve that does not cross over itself and is sufficiently well behaved. The rigor involved in defining what we mean by "sufficiently well behaved" is omitted here for brevity. Let the curve C be described parametrically by a function $\gamma: [0,1] \to \mathbb{C}$ with parameter t varying from zero to one, and assume that it meets our requirements for it to be "sufficiently well behaved" (in the language of analysis γ be a rectifiable path). If $f(z)$ is the function of a complex variable z the value of the function for any point on the curve is $f(\gamma(t))$. The line integral of f $along$ C is defined as (and denoted by)

$$\int_C f = \int_C f(z)\, dz = \int_0^1 f(\gamma(t)) d\gamma$$

To see how the evaluation works we can consider $\gamma(t) = e^{it} = \cos t + i \sin t$ which is a path along a unit circle centered at the origin as t varies over $[0,2\pi]$. We know that $d\gamma = ie^{it}dt$. Now, if $f(z) = \frac{1}{z}; z \neq 0$ then the integral can be easily evaluated as $\int_C z^{-1}\, dz = \int_0^{2\pi} e^{-it}(i\, e^{it})dt = 2\pi i$. If we examine $f(z) = z^m; m \geq 0, m\ is\ an\ integer$ the calculation changes and it is easy to see that the answer is zero. Contour integrals have interesting behaviors when the closed curve C encloses "singularities" of function $f(z)$ such as what happened when we tried integrating $f(z) = \frac{1}{z}$ around the unit circle. This function z^{-1} had a "singularity" at $z = 0$ and resulted in non-zero final answer while the function $z^m; m > 0$ does not have a singularity inside the unit circle, and the corresponding integral is zero. It turns out that this behavior of the function z^{-1} deserves some more attention. Let us see what happens to z^{-2} in the same contour integral. $\int_C z^{-2}\,dz = \int_0^{2\pi} e^{-2it}(i\,e^{it})dt = \int_0^{2\pi} e^{-it}(i\,)dt = (i)\frac{e^{-it}}{-i}\Big)_0^{2\pi} = 0$. Thus, the non-zero contribution to the integral is only by $1/z$ term and not from $1/z^m$ terms where $m \neq 1\ is\ positive$. One other surprising fact about this result is that the "curve" over which we are integrating the function is away from the point $z = 0$. Still, somehow that integral has information about the behavior of the function at $z = 0$! (In layman terms this would be something like making a statement on what is happening in downtown by taking a car ride around the city never actually going to downtown!). In complex analysis, it is also shown that if instead of a circle we integrated on an ellipse around the origin the function $\frac{1}{z}$ would still give the answer as $2\pi i$! In fact, if we keep "deforming" the circular curve to anything else (sufficiently well behaved) as long as we don't cross the origin in that process or make the curve pinch or cross over itself, the answer will remain $2\pi i$ for $f(z) = z^{-1}$! This is certainly surprising and fascinating. The integral of $\frac{1}{z}$ along curves going round the origin are characterized by the $1/z$ behavior at the origin. This observation is so critical that there is a special attribute defined for functions, called "residue" when investigating points of singularity. For example, if $f(z)$ has a series expansion near point a given below

$$f(z) = \frac{b_0}{(z-a)^m} + \cdots + \frac{b_{m-1}}{z-a} + \sum_{k=0}^{\infty} b_{m+k}(z-a)^k$$

The coefficient b_{m-1} is called the residue of $f(z)$ at $z = a$ and carries special importance in evaluating line integral of $f(z)$ along a closed curve that may encompass point $z = a$. While there is no reason here to engage in details of how residues are calculated using analytical techniques, the attention is drawn to the fact that in line integrals encompassing points of singularity the contribution to the integrals primarily comes from singularities inside the curve and in particular from residues at the singular points. This is the essence of what is known as the Residue Theorem. The formal statement of the theorem is as follows –

Theorem: If C is a simple closed curve in the complex plane, the contour integral of a function $f(z)$ along C is given by

$$\int_C f(z)dz = 2\pi i \sum Res(f, a)$$

Where $Res(f, a)$ denotes residue of f at $z = a$, the summation is to be carried out over all singular points $z = a$ in the interior of (enclosed by) the curve C.

Emotional Inspiration

The poem attempts to focus attention on some key aspects of the residue theorem. It draws parallels between those facets and our emotional experiences in key life-changing events. The contribution to the line integrals is primarily from singular points where the function "blows up". The poem draws attention to the fact that when things go wrong in our lives (blow up), they usually lead us to question our fundamental premise. Those are the most significant learning experiences that elevate us to a more enlightened state. The second parallel being drawn is to appeal to our "inner workings" that dictate who we are. Just as the contribution to line integrals is from the interior of the enclosing curve, our interior dictates our behavior and its manifestations. Finally, the poem alludes to the concept of a residue in the sense of the legacy we leave behind as the signature of our lives.

♦

Louville's Theorem

Theorem: Bounded entire functions are constants.

As polynomials depart, marching to infinity
A class of functions awaits
To welcome them to the fraternity

Title Analytical, is given a treatment special
Their riches in this world are measured with a differential

Derivatives of sorts, cannot kill them any more
Whichever number you chose,
They can differentiate some more!

This currency of powers has caused some greed
Those with compact support now desired to be freed

Being real and analytical is not enough to quench the thirst
To the world of complex functions,
They said, "Let's see who gets their first!"

The world of complex functions would likely
Satisfy their greed
For a mere first derivative,
There were infinite options indeed!

Unaware of nature, that the "i" brings a strange structure
Single differentiability demanded the the C^{∞} Feature!

Why don't we change the gear? (they thought)
Let's conquer the Rieman's sphere
The coveted title was the "Function Entire"!

Wiggle wiggle wiggle was now the new function's struggle
In all of the directions, it had no choice but to bubble

Growing this way to infinity was exhausting it found
How nice would it be to establish a bound!

In searching for a bound, Mr Louville's brilliance found
That reduced to a constant was now
The Entire Function's sound!

♠

Louville's Theorem
Mathematical Context:

Louville's theorem is another one of the celebrated and powerful theorems in complex analysis. To understand the theorem's content, a brief discussion of real and complex analytical functions is needed.

A real-valued function $f(x)$ of a real variable, x is said to be analytic if it can be expressed as a power series in some neighborhood (region) on the real line –

$$f(x) = \sum_{n=0}^{\infty} c_n x^n$$

Equivalently, the power series expansion could be around a point $x = a$ and expressed as

$$f(x) = \sum_{n=0}^{\infty} c_n (x - a)^n$$

The idea is that such functions "behave like polynomials" in the neighborhood where they are analytic. Anyone familiar with analysis and college-level calculus can relate to such expressions in terms of Taylor series of a function using derivatives –

$$f(a + h) = f(a) + f'(a)h + \frac{f''(a)}{2!}h^2 + \cdots$$

Analytical functions, under certain convergence criteria (e.g., uniform convergence), are sufficiently well behaved to carry out operations similar to those in polynomials. Examples are "term-by-term differentiation of power series" for

$f'(x)$ etc. to give $f^k(x) = \sum_{n=k}^{\infty} n(n-1)\dots(n-k+1)c_n x^{n-k}$ or coefficient multiplications for the product of two analytical functions. One may be tempted to think, based on Taylor series expansion, that if a function is infinitely differentiable (i.e., in class C^{∞}), then it will be analytic. It turns out that this is not true. An example is the following function in figure 18, which is infinitely differentiable at $x = 0$, but it is not analytic at $x = 0$. It is not too difficult to show that all its derivatives are zero at $x = 0$ (in layman terms, it goes to zero very-very smoothly)

$$g(x) = \begin{cases} 0, & x \leq 0 \\ e^{-\frac{1}{x^2}}, & x > 0 \end{cases}$$

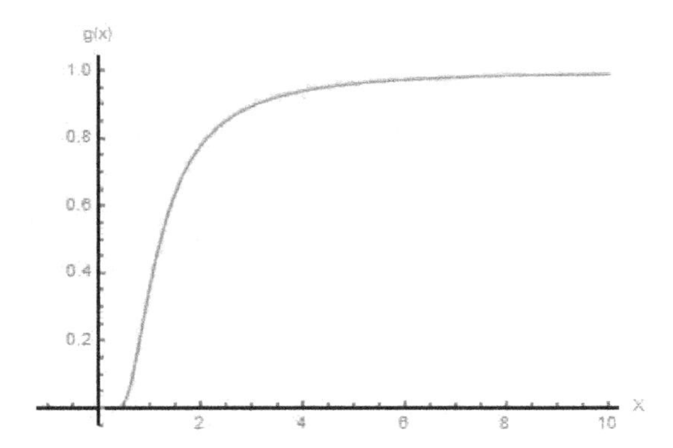

Figure 18. A function that is infinitely differentiable at x=0 but not analytic at x=0

This points to a certain behavior of analytic functions around points where the function attains zero values (zeros of analytical functions). It turns out that analytic functions cannot have zeros that are "clustered" (e.g., zero over an interval) and the functions "keep wiggling" like polynomials. Following the same argument, there are no functions in the class C_c^{∞} (read as "see infinity with compact support") that are analytical over the real line. The term compact support means that the function is non-zero only over a “compact set” (think of a closed interval as an example of a compact set on the real line). For more details, the reader can refer to graduate texts in real analysis, such as “Principles of Mathematical Analysis by Walter Rudin.” In layman terms, the functions such as $g(x)$ above are “nice and smooth,” but they are not “nice enough to be analytic” and don’t “behave like polynomials.” My subjective use of the words “nice” and “nice enough” here is intentional.

Now, let us see what happens when we extend this to complex valued functions of a complex variable. In complex analysis a class of analytic functions is formed by the complex functions of a complex variable which possess a derivative wherever the function is defined. Now, this requirement seems like a very “simple demand” that if we want $f(z)$ to be a complex analytic function, all we are asking is that the derivative should exist in the complex plane (with $complex\ h$) wherever the function is defined –

$$f'(z) = \lim_{h \to 0} \frac{f(z+h) - f(z)}{h}$$

This comes as a surprise when coming from “the world of real-valued functions of a real variable.” On the real line, the demand for the existence of a derivative means that a similar limit should exist when $h \to 0$ on the real line. There are two directions available for real variable h to approach zero, and the two limits should match. Figure 19 illustrates a real function such that the derivative exists for all but one point. The point where the derivative fails to exist is where limit as $h \to 0^+$ (i.e. $h > 0$) is not in agreement with the limit as $h \to 0^-$ (i.e. $h < 0$).

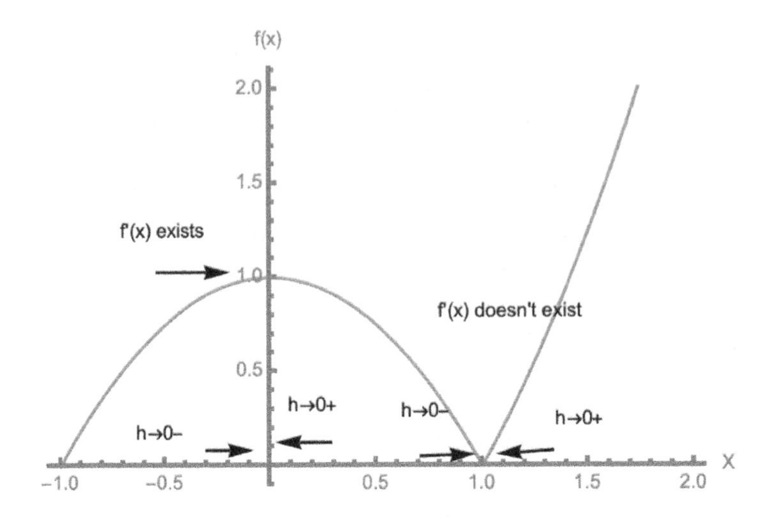

Figure 19. Real valued function, derivative fails to exist at x=1

When you demand that a complex function be differentiable, $h \to 0$ can proceed along any of the infinitely many paths available in a complex plane, unlike the real line where h can approach zero only in one of the two directions. One such complicated path that can be taken by h in approaching zero in the complex plane is shown in figure 20.

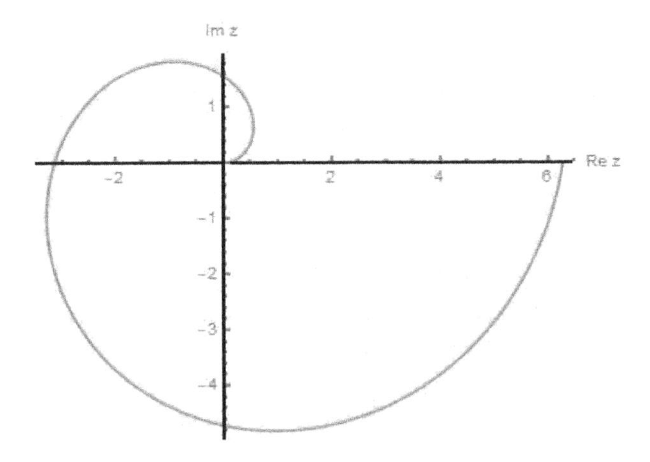

Figure 20. One possible complicated path taken by $h \to 0$ in a complex plane.

It may be thought that the situation would be similar in the case where we consider functions on two dimensional real space $\mathbb{R}^2$, i.e., $Q(x,y) = (u(x,y), v(x,y))$. It would seem that differentiability in $\mathbb{R}^2$ would face the same limitation since two-dimensional increment $\boldsymbol{dx} = (\Delta x, \Delta y)$ could approach zero in infinitely many ways. However, to our surprise (or not), it turns out that demanding a function to be "complex differentiable" is much more stringent than demanding that an equivalent function in $\mathbb{R}^2$ be differentiable. This is because the complex plane also has an underlying algebraic structure imposed by $i = \sqrt{-1}$. If $f(z) = f(x + iy) = u(x,y) + iv(x,y)$ then it can be shown that for $f'(z)$ to exist $u(x,y) and\ v(x,y)$ must satisfy what are called Cauchy-Riemann conditions $\frac{\partial u}{\partial x} = \frac{\partial v}{\partial y}\ and\ \frac{\partial u}{\partial y} = -\frac{\partial v}{\partial x}$. There is no such requirement for $\mathbb{R}^2$ −differentiability. The function $r(x,y) = (x, -y)$ can be seen to be not differentiable as a complex function since it does not satisfy Cauchy-Riemann conditions, but it is differentiable as a function in $\mathbb{R}^2$ (it is a mere reflection of the plane). The matrix of its partial derivatives is given by –

$$D_r = \begin{pmatrix} \partial u/\partial x & \partial u/\partial y \\ \partial v/\partial x & \partial v/\partial y \end{pmatrix} = \begin{pmatrix} 1 & 0 \\ 0 & -1 \end{pmatrix}; \frac{\partial u}{\partial x} \neq \frac{\partial v}{\partial y}$$

Let us extend things by one more step. The next result is nothing short of being stunning, and I can say that when I first encountered it as a student, I found it almost unbelievable. It is shown in complex analysis that if a complex function is analytic, its derivative is analytic. Yes, you read that right. There is no such thing in real functions: if it is differentiable, then the derivative is differentiable! When you asked for a complex function to be differentiable in our layman terms, you effectively "asked for a lot" because for the complex function to be once differentiable, it needs to be effectively differentiable infinitely!

There are a few noble questions that may now be asked. Are there complex functions that are analytic everywhere in the complex plane? The answer is, of course, yes, and an example would be the function $f(z) = e^z$. A function that is analytic everywhere in the complex plane is called an entire function. The poem has a reference to "Riemann Sphere," which is a neat representation of an entire complex plane on a sphere when "point at infinity" is augmented to the complex plane and placed at the "north pole" of the sphere. Its representation is shown in figure 21.

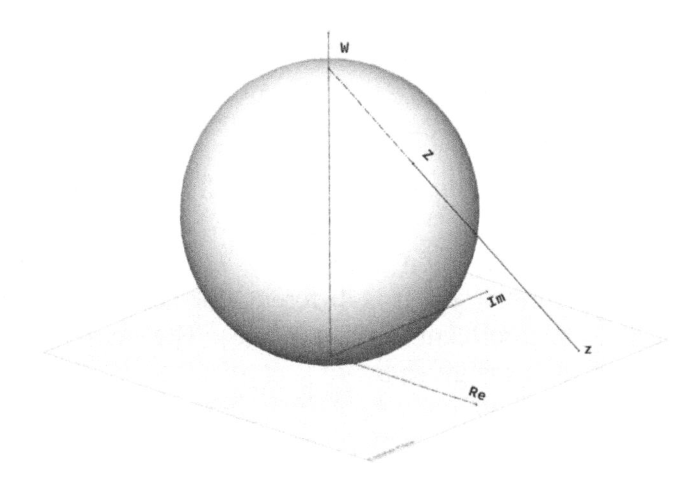

Figure 21. Representation of Riemann Sphere

Taking our noble questions further, how about functions that are analytic everywhere but remain bounded like what we have on the real line with trigonometric functions such as $\sin x, \cos x$? Louville's theorem shows that if the complex function is demanded to be an entire function and remain bounded, it must be a constant! When you asked for the complex function to be analytic everywhere and remain bounded in layman terms, you asked for so much that it effectively lost its variations and is reduced to a constant!! For rigorous details and discussion, the reader should consult graduate texts in complex analysis such as "Complex Analysis by Lars V. Ahlfors."

I feel compelled to add a few more comments on the side due to my personal experience. In physical sciences, many times, analysis is carried out by modeling certain fields using complex analytic functions. An example would be modeling stress fields near a crack tip using complex analytic functions. When dealing with complicated situations such as cracks at an interface, the analysis begins by representing stress fields through complex analytic functions (see, for example, graduate texts in fracture mechanics such as "Cracks and Fracture by K. B. Broeberg"). By the time the statement is made that "let the stress fields be represented by complex analytic functions" based on the above, we should be alerted that we have already asked for these fields to be "super nice" and then look at the rest of the analysis and results. This pause and awareness of the flag are often missed as a student of the subject (I certainly did the first time) since we are in a rush to get to the expressions for quantities of interest in physics! Oh, and yes, Louville's theorem is indeed used to analyze stress fields in interface fracture in case you were wondering!!

Emotional Inspiration

The poem is written with a backdrop of greed and blind effort for satiating desires. The parallels drawn are between attempting to enhance analytic functions with a more rich structure and chasing worldly recognition and wealth to be treated special. Louville's theorem, when viewed from this perspective, does have the same flavor as that in saying, "excess of anything is bad."

♦

The Central Limit Theorem

The morning dew could be felt beneath
As tender greens were caressing my feet

In a gentle glide, my mind had wandered
Seeking the truth, I had long upon pondered

The morning breeze had brought some clarity
The game of my fate was ... probability!

Coins and balls and tosses and dice
Behind the veil was hiding... a truth concise!

Sometimes uniform, sometimes binomial
Pain and pleasure were part of survival!

When a mate for my soul had hinted its arrival
Nothing in the day could be 'logged as normal'

Harmony of hearts is one of those specials
Transcend it will, the distribution of exponentials!

Pumping of my heart was the weakest of the links
Weibul's analysis had shown its kinks

But passion and heartbreaks are experiences akin
I am a mere sample, said statistics with a grin!

The rising of the morning sun had shown me the light
Central Limit Theorem was the real delight!

The crisis of my identity was the toughest inner fight
Like several of those distributions,
I struggled to describe myself right!

Minds and thoughts and bodies and souls
In a crisis of identity, are searching for goals

Averaging of averages reveal an enlightening feature
Samples infinite with one normal soul...
Is our essential nature!

Central Limit Theorem Mathematical Context:

Central Limit Theorem (CLT) is one of the most significant theorems in statistics and has many practical implications. The theorem is about a probability distribution called the Normal distribution (The bell curve). To understand the significance of normal distribution and CLT alluded to in the poem, it is worthwhile to briefly ponder probability and statistics and a few key statistical distributions. The following passages attempt to briefly outline the relevant concepts and the emotional journey I experienced when learning them as a student and thinking about them as an instructor.

Typical discussion of a probability distribution starts with events that are declared as random. Typical academic examples for random events are a coin toss, throw of a dice, or some random draw from a card deck. While these satisfy our need to have a framework under which we analyze random events and probability, whenever I have engaged in these discussions as a student or as an instructor, I have always wondered later in contemplation – "Are there events that are truly random? Or we use it as a label for things we don't understand?". I know that this is a philosophical question, and there are numerous discussions that one can find on the topic. However, it does not take away the merit of the question and an overwhelming emotional reaction to this question personally.

One of the places where the randomness of the outcome is central to the place's very existence is a casino. It is not surprising then that French mathematician de Moivre discovered the Normal distribution while working in a casino, helping some rich clients figure out patterns and chances. It was supposedly later refined by great minds of the time – Gauss and Laplace. More than the chronological account of the history, discovering a distribution in a casino that later became so central to sciences and several branches of research have fascinated me personally.

In fact, before jumping to appreciate the Normal distribution, I have also found myself in a state of pause when questioning myself – would I have thought that there is a "pattern" to events that are seemingly random in occurrence? Or would I have simply accepted them as something of a chance which I can't explain and moved on? In this pause, the very idea of describing the seemingly random events using a concept of a distribution and seeking an equation to describe the pattern has felt like a stroke of brilliance, let alone the shock and awe of someone finding such an equation in a casino, and then it being of central importance to sciences and research across several branches.

In statistical science, several probability distributions are available as tools to describe events that we categorize as random. Bernoulli trials describing a coin toss leading to Binomial Distribution is a good starting point. As the number of trials becomes large, Binomial coefficients' characteristic bell-shaped curve emerges as the bell curve describing the Normal distribution. Further, there are distributions of different kinds with an associated character. This can be briefly described informally as below (not meant to be an exhaustive list)

1. Poisson Distribution: defect counts (e.g., defects in solids), customer arrival in a store.
2. Binomial Distribution: Coin tosses – biased or unbiased, pass/fail outcomes, number of defective parts in a lot.
3. Uniform Distribution over an interval: Natural description where all outcomes over a range of values are equally likely.

4. Exponential distribution: Constant rate of failures in parts, e.g., electronics, arrival times, or interval between events.
5. Weibul Distribution: Distribution of extreme values or events where the weakest link governs failure.
6. Lognormal Distribution: Its construct seems somewhat "artificial," demanding that the random variable's logarithm has a normal distribution. However, several applications have been found in sciences where lognormal distribution is a better descriptor of the random event, e.g., to describe survival times after cancer.

Now each of the distributions has a different shape describing how certain events or values are more likely to occur than the other except in uniform distribution where all values in the interval are equally likely. For standard normal distribution (Figure 22), the center (value zero) is more likely than away from the center. Such would be the case if we asked 20 operators to measure the length of a machined part with a calliper. They won't all measure the same value, but the values they obtain will "cluster" around a "mean" value in bell-shape. The deviations from the mean will have zero and vicinity as the most likely outcome.

$$f(x) = \frac{1}{\sqrt{2\pi}} e^{-\frac{1}{2}x^2}$$

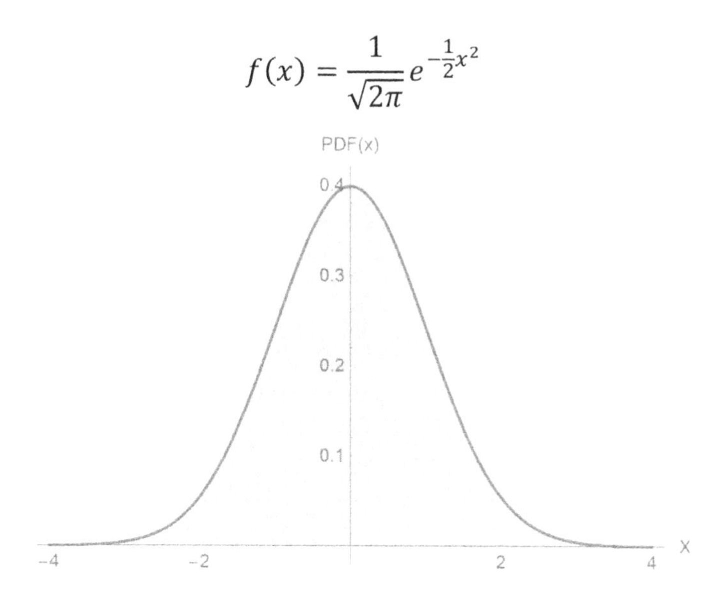

Figure 22. Standard Normal Distribution

Now, consider the experiment where we pick one of the distributions and randomly draw a sample from the population that obeys this distribution. An example would be to draw say 10 (sample size =10) random values from a uniform distribution over the interval [0,1]. Then find the mean of the ten values. We can repeat this with sample sizes 10, 100, 1000, 10000, etc. Every time we calculate the mean of the sample. As sample sizes grow, what do we expect the mean to do? We expect that it will approach ½ since that is buried in the statement that all values in [0,1] are equally likely. So as many values occur on the left of ½ will occur on the right of ½ when enough draws have taken place. What can we say about "In what way will all these mean values cluster around ½ ?". CLT answers that question saying that the clustering has the shape of normal distribution. Further, it also claims that the distribution of these "sample means" is a normal distribution *regardless of the parent distribution*. The result of such a numerical experiment (up to n=1000) is shown in figure 23

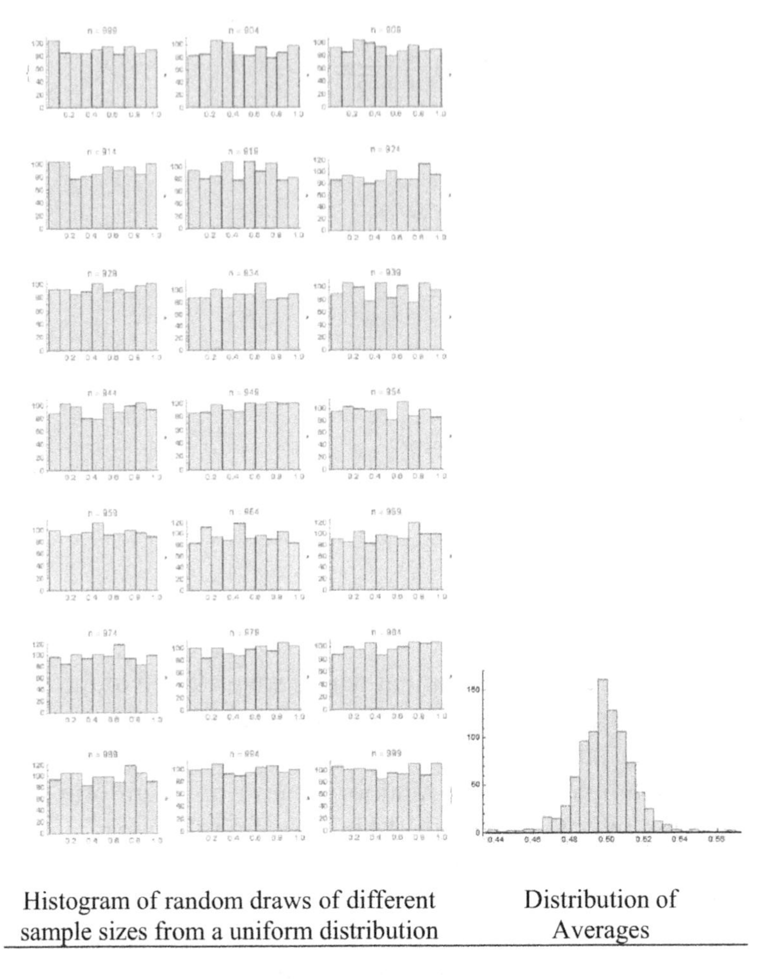

Figure 23. Numerical experiment demonstrating CLT for uniform distribution. The table of histograms shows draws with different samples sizes. Distribution of averages is obtained by taking mean values of the draws up to n=1000.

A formal statement of the CLT is as follows –

<u>Theorem (CLT)</u>: Let $X_1, X_2, \ldots, X_n$ be a random sample of size n taken from a population (finite or infinite) with mean μ and standard deviation σ. Define $\bar{X}$ to be the sample

mean. Define another random variable $Z = \left(\frac{\bar{X}-\mu}{(\sigma/\sqrt{n})}\right)$. Then in the limit, as n tends to infinity distribution of Z is a standard normal distribution. (Regardless of the distribution of X)

The "surprise" here is the ubiquitous normal distribution occurrence starting from any parent distribution when sample means are considered. Further, the statement of CLT identifies the "rate" of convergence to be in inverse proportion to $\sqrt{n}$ as the sample size increases. While those who are mathematically sharp will argue that it is not really "surprising" that there is clustering around the population mean, the theorem's proof is not simple. The fact that a concrete statement can be made about the "rate of convergence dependent on $\sqrt{n}$" and "shape of clustering" of sample means to population means based on sample size is not obvious. For instance, as a student, one would not know whether to "expect" the convergence to be at the rate $1/n$, $1/n^2$ or $1/\sqrt{n}$. I have found myself wondering – why would all distributions (under some reasonable conditions) in the averaging scheme be "reduced to normal"? Why is the shape of clustering of means described well by ae^{-bx^2}? The answers to these questions, of course, are found in the proof, but that does not take away the awe of such occurrence and the appreciation of the brilliance in discovering this fact.

Emotional Inspiration

The poem ventures gently in contemplation, where the central query is whether our fate is a game of probability. I have personally found it challenging to reconcile life events as random. Upon scrutiny of personal successes and failures, I have felt that effort certainly has a cardinal role to play in both, but I could not ignore the presence of chance events. There are numerous choices that we make along the way, which I cannot claim with certainty to be an outcome of a deterministic process. I find that my maturity of life experiences and wisdom are not where I can make any such claim to the elements of "the truth." Such conflicted states have been more pronounced for me in the reconciliation of experiences that led to some kind of hardship, including disappointments, failures, and heartbreaks.

Such contemplation had also changed my view of when my performance led to success – again, *both* effort and chance have mattered here. For me, the best way to reconcile these without having the burden of "the truth" has been to accept them as transcendental chance elements, present but not visible to me. They affect the balance in the equation purely conceived based on efforts and data - sometimes favorable and sometimes not. It has been easier to think of self as a statistical sample rather than claim significance and ownership with the burden of "the truth" beyond my reach. The emotional appeal of the CLT for me has been the ubiquitous appearance of normal distribution regardless of which parent distribution you start with (in the averaging process). It makes me look at commonality in individuals around me who influence my life in some form or the other every day.

♦

A Living Bayesian

Early in one summer
The morning hour had arrived with some thunder
Startled and disturbed, I looked out of the window
The sun was yet to arrive... why am I up? I wondered

My neighbor's cat then just knocked on the door
At this hour?
What an unusual time! I thought
Around this time, I usually snore.

That day stood out from the rest
Disturbing my expectations and pattern
Thunder had struck with some zest

Why was it not like yesterday?
And the day before?
Is there a reason for things to be the same?
In response, asked my core.

This simple question
Had sent chills down my spine
When I see 'unusual',
How do I find a definite cause to assign?

Illusions of my making, in a moment, had then shattered
In every occurrence, significant or insignificant
My efforts, wisdom, choices and along with it
Coincidences and my luck
All seemed to have mattered

Did I learn and progress by regression and correlation?
Was my inner making a work of mere determination?
Or was my present reality
Always a Bayesian creation?

Why did I tie effort and success?
In one thread as cause and effect?
It dawned upon me in the dark morning hour
That, in my perception, lied some defect.

The lost sailor at sea the previous night
Was by his fate, found and rescued
The key to my transformation lied in seeing then
How his search was to be probabilistically viewed

A story from the 1740s
Then flashed on my ceiling
With open eyes, I looked inside,
My pride needed some healing

Beliefs and truths are intertwined
In the fabric of my everyday dealing
I was and am a living Bayesian
Was a new and humble feeling.

When the data changes,
I try to change my belief
Instead of carrying the burden of certainty
I strive for this evolution and long for the relief

Such untimely thunders, in life I thought,
Provide valuable pauses
Now I know why the centuries-old "Doctrine of Chances."
Asked us to step away from certainty and
Think 'probability of causes'

♠

A Living Bayesian Mathematical Context:

Bayes' Theorem is one of the most significant theorems in probability theory and is often referred to as a theorem in inverse probability. The theorem is named after an English Statistician Thomas Bayes. We can first look at mathematical statements associated with the theorem –

Theorem: If we have a collection of hypotheses (or causes) $H_1, H_2, \ldots, H_n$ which are mutually exclusive and exhaustive, i.e., every sample point belongs to one and only one among the H_i we have

$$P\{H_k|A\} = \frac{P\{A|H_k\}P\{H_k\}}{P\{A\}} = \frac{P\{A|H_k\}P\{H_k\}}{\sum_{j=1}^{n} P\{A|H_j\}P\{H_j\}}$$

$$Definition: P\{A|B\}$$
$$= Probability\ of\ event\ A\ given\ that\ B\ has\ taken\ palce$$

This theorem has a rich history. After its discovery by Thomas Bayes, it is fair to say that it took a couple of centuries for its significance to be accepted by scientists and statisticians.

When looked at in the finished form given above, the implication of the theorem is often missed. I am guilty of missing the significance when reading the above statement as a student. When I first saw this in the classroom, it certainly appeared like some jugglery of mathematical formulas and algebraic trickery. The ignorance was to the point that I wasn't sure why it carried someone's name with it. Without engaging in the calculations and answers, I would like to state two problems in probability theory below: one is often what you encounter in early probability lessons, and the second, not so often –

Problem 1: Let three bags A, B, C contain white and black balls listed as follows –

Color/Bag	A	B	C
White	a_1	a_2	a_3
Black	b_1	b_2	b_3

A bag is chosen at random, and a ball is drawn from it at random. What is the probability that the ball is white?

Problem 2: Let three bags A, B, C contain white and black balls listed as follows –

Color/Bag	A	B	C
White	a_1	a_2	a_3
Black	b_1	b_2	b_3

A bag is chosen at random, and a ball is drawn from it at random. The ball is found to be white. What is the probability that it came from bag A?

If you have been a sincere enough student of probability theory, you have dealt with problems of type 1 in early classes. The second problem is not presented in classrooms often in the first introduction.

You may say, "OK, yeah. Problem 2 is somewhat more complicated than problem 1. I get it!" – and right there, you missed out on the significance of Problem 2 just like I did as a student. Problem 2 is not just a little more difficult, but it is of fundamentally different character than problem 1. Problem 2 asks to calculate the probability of causes when evidence is presented, while problem 1 asks us to calculate probability of outcome when causes are known. Problem 2 is equivalent in the character of asking the following – I know that MIT students do well in their technical professions overall. Is it due to the teaching quality at MIT, or were they good enough to begin with? You can then construct a

2x2 table of good/bad student and good/bad teaching with good/bad performance in a profession as an entry in each box. Do this as a thought experiment and ask – where does your belief lie? Can you quantify it? If needed, you should take a pause here. I did not take that pause as a student.

There are several papers written and lectures available on Bayes' Theorem and its applications. A simple Google query "Bayes' Theorem" today resulted in 11.9 million hits! There is no need to present calculations and details here since the interested reader can find more comprehensive coverage on these in probability and statistics books – undergraduate and graduate. A few things worth mentioning here are related to this theorem's development and are related to my emotional journey in learning this theorem.

When looking at the historical account such as the one presented in "The theory that would not die" by Sharon Bertsch McGrayne, the discovery of the theorem was made by Thomas Bayes sometime in the 1740s and then mysteriously abandoned. It was reported in his famous posthumous paper "An essay towards solving a Problem in the Doctrine of Chances." It was rediscovered independently by a far more renowned man, Pierre Simon Laplace, who gave it the modern mathematical form. Laplace seems to have stated the observation as a principle rather than in a mathematical formula, stating that the probability of a cause given the event's occurrence is proportional to the probability of the event given the cause. I needed a pause here to think if this statement is intuitive for me. In the above problem 2, if bag A did not have any white balls, and a white ball was found, the probability that it came from bag A would be zero. So, there is a dependence, but is it obvious that the probability of cause (bag A) given the occurrence (white ball) is *proportional* to the probability of occurrence (white ball) given the cause (bag A)? I struggled. When one thinks of $P(A \cap B) =$

$P(A|B)P(B) = P(B|A)P(A)$ the claim looks simple; however, that seems to be because the set-theoretic thinking is served to us on a "silver plate," and the rest is algebraic trickery. Without that, it remained difficult for me to align with Laplace's statement and associated intuition.

In the 20th century, statisticians noted Bayes' rule and vilified both the method and its adherents, seemingly due to the framework of belief that gets associated with the claim. As it turns out, there were several practical problems where the rule kept demonstrating its value. It seems to have taken a long time, even for the intellectuals, to accept the framework to think in terms of "probability of causes" rather than thinking in terms of certainty, despite its value demonstrated in practical applications.

Emotional Inspiration

The poem is about the process of internalizing a result, such as Bayes' theorem, after it has been studied and understood for its academic content. I find that the process of learning significant results involves two distinct parts, each of which may have steps involved that are different for everyone. In my experience, understanding a principle or a result for what it states is different from having it internalized to the point where it can be claimed to be part of "your knowledge" or something "you understand." This is, of course, true of non-mathematical aspects of learning as well. It is like the difference between understanding that "speaking truth is beneficial" as a principle and knowing individually the benefits of speaking the truth and downsides of not being truthful. For the second part, a certain level of experimentation or scrutiny, with and without the truth, seems necessary.

Bayes' theorem's most significant impression for me has been about the paradigm shift in the framework where we have to start thinking in terms of probability of causes instead of thinking deterministically. It took me some effort to accept incomplete information as a norm rather than an exception or limitation. I have seen the statements in the historic evolution of the theorem to this effect. However, they did not cause me to reexamine my values. The example presented earlier where you are asked to compute "probability that the ball came from bag A" remained an academic exercise - a skill which I had to learn out of interest. I heard stories of how impressive Bayes' theorem's use was in cracking enigma, developing search algorithms in case of lost sailors at sea, and numerous such examples.

There is no shortage of such examples and applications. Only when the query became personal about why and how I attribute credit or blame for my successes and failures to my efforts or otherwise, that the probability of causes made sense to me as a person. I had and still have trouble with causality when it comes to effort and failure. With success, I seem to be more willing to consider effort as the cause for the result. I came face to face with my limitation in owning my success and failures – that is when I was ready to accept that there were other factors whose contribution I *certainly did not know*. Dealing with incomplete information is something I had done throughout as my practiced way of development, even when I was busy claiming ownership of a fairy tale about my success whenever it occurred - a truth that was difficult to accept.

A consequence of that is a seismic shift in perspective on how I view my evolution and development. I was more comfortable thinking of my development in terms of regression, correlation, and building upon the patterns I observed, extrapolating, and taking the next step. The questions regarding success, failure, and causality make me think of the development as Bayesian, where I evolve my belief while gathering data where the next step can be a leap of faith. In one case, I feel like the ship captain, and the other case makes me feel like I am on a raft.

The question, the statement, and the theorem's content had a reflection inside of me that was personal enough only after this scrutiny.

♦

The Möbius Strip

Some lovely sweet talks
Had lingered in my heart
Blond hair and blue eyes
Were tearing me apart

Her curly blond hair
Came with simple brown eyes
The brunette friend of mine, though,
Had supreme blue eyes

My mind had now wandered
Altering the reality
None of the thoughts that night
Would bring me any clarity

My hormones that night
Had taken center stage
Mathematics of love
Needed a German math page!

Two opposing normals
Could be seamlessly joined
The solution to my problem
Only Möbius could find!

A twist like Möbius
Will confuse left and right,
With confidence, I thought
I can seduce both overnight!

The girls were truly smart
They knew very well this art
Joining hands, they said
It's time to blow him apart

They came with a congregation
Introducing a new dimension
With racing of my heart
My head was in gyration

My fascination for Möbius
Was about to get some cut
With orientations clear
I ran to save my butt.

I ran with perspiration
This was a mistaken application
The twist in the Möbius Strip
Had ruined my summer vacation!

♠

Möbius Strip
Mathematical Context:

I will start with a simple tricky riddle from childhood. You are supposed to answer this question in one word – On what side of the coffee mug is the handle? Often the reaction to this question from kids is "it depends," "it depends on how the mug is placed relative to the person," and then if you are the smart one who is asking the question, you would stretch and say, "No, these are many words. Remember – one word!". A few kids lose hope that this is indeed a sensible riddle and start suspecting that this is some stupid riddle. Then the final answer is revealed – "outside!". After many years of schooling, one fine day, I was struck with this riddle again, throwing me into a very long pause because what the answer shows is that the coffee mug indeed has two sides – an inside and an outside. Do all surfaces have two sides?

I would have never asked this question until I saw what the business of "orientability" of a surface is about. Common surfaces we encounter always have two sides. The mathematical idealization of a "surface" that we think of also carries this notion of "sides" defined by normal vectors to the surface. There are two possible normal vectors at each point on the surface. If we consider "painting" the surface, two different colors can be applied to the two sides. If you are an ant crawling on this surface, there is a "top side" and a "bottom-side," and you cannot go from the top side to the bottom side without a "discontinuous transition" such as an ant crossing over the edge of the coffee mug to go from "inside" to "outside." In 1858 German mathematician August Möbius discovered a "non-orientable" surface, i.e., it does not have two sides. It only has "one side"! The depiction of this surface is shown in figure 24.

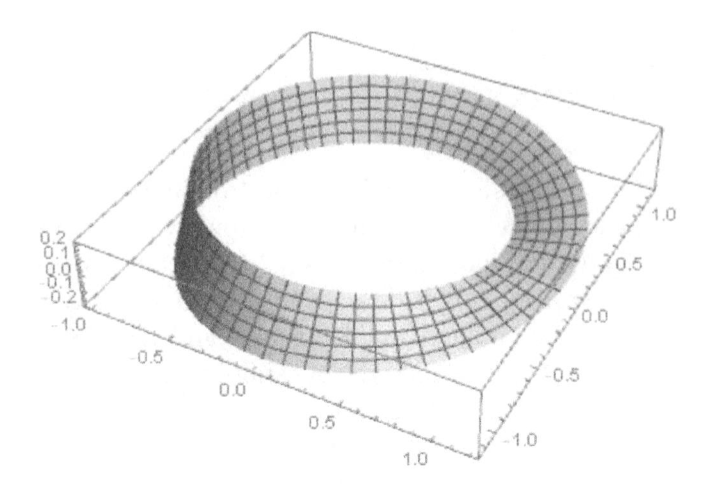

Figure 24. Depiction of Mobius Strip

This strip is easily formed by taking a "band," cutting it into a strip, giving one end half a twist, and re-attaching. The key is that this strip now has "only one side" in the sense that if you start painting it, the entire strip will get painted with the same color – no two colors, for there are no "two sides." Suppose you are a "two-dimensional" insect living on this strip when you travel around. In that case, you can smoothly transition from left-handed to right-handed without a discontinuous transition, or an insect can crawl and make its orientation "flip" without having to go through a discontinuous transition like crossing over an edge. One key observation is that if you cut the Möbius strip along the middle, the resulting strip will effectively have "two twists" and be orientable. Anyone can easily verify this. It is worth noting that the Möbius strip is not a "true surface" since it is non-orientable.

It is the simplest non-orientable surface. It is essentially "two-dimensional" but acquires its unique character only because it is "embedded" in the three-dimensional space, i.e., the "twist" is in the third dimension. Why is this comment relevant? If you are a "two-dimensional" insect living on the

Möbius strip, you can experience a smooth change of orientation from left-handed to right-handed but cannot conceive the twist in the third dimension. This prompts the question – can there be such a phenomenon that we experience in 3D, but its explanation lies in the fourth dimension? While this is a very interesting question to ponder over, a geometric object conceived in this manner is called the Klein Bottle, named after German mathematician Felix Klein, who described it in 1882.

Emotional Inspiration

I prefer to leave it to the original poetic expression without further comments.

♦

The Divergence Theorem

$$\int_{\partial\Omega} \vec{V} \cdot \vec{n}\, ds = \int_{\Omega} \nabla \cdot \vec{V}\, dv$$

A lad from Nottingshire,
Had a truly unusual desire
With no teacher found around,
He was playing with mathematical fire.

They called him a Baker's son
Housing a windmill, the bread was won
Unaware was Mr. Green
Of the incredible work, he had done!

Without fame, he had died,
Lord Kelvin restored that pride
In the mystery of the laws of nature
Great insights Green's work could provide

Secrets were revealed with some class
The name on the theorem was Gauss
Told with a proof Ostrogadskii
How boundaries of domains are crossed

Gauss' divergent notion
Is the grammar of conservation
In moments of pain and loss
It is a means of true consolation

In the moments of turmoil and churns
It's the inside of us that burns
The truth be told by Gauss...
It is with fluxes at boundaries that our fate turns!

♠

Divergence Theorem
Mathematical Context:

The divergence theorem is important in vector calculus and finds its application in the derivation of governing equations in different branches of physical sciences such as fluid mechanics, heat transfer, and electrostatics, to name a few. A typical mathematical physics student will encounter these in early education. The content of the poem is motivated from a historical account of the discovery of the divergence theorem as outlined in "A History of the Divergence Theorem, by C. H. Stolze published in Historia Mathematica, 1978, pp437-442" and my emotional journey as I learned the theorem and demonstrated its use as an instructor. The mathematical significance of the divergence theorem cannot be understated. As evident, the theorem carries the name Gauss Divergence Theorem named after arguably one of the greatest mathematicians – Carl F. Gauss.

To provide the mathematical context, I will start with the simplest form of the theorem, which, when stated, almost seems pointless to anyone having taken a course in basic integral calculus. The purpose of the following passages is to point to some key aspects alluded to in the poem rather than giving academic details of the theorem.

Using the definition of integral as "anti-derivative" and carrying out a definite integral –

$$\int_{a}^{b} \frac{df}{dx}\, dx = f(b) - f(a)$$

Those who have encountered the theorem in their formal training will, of course, recognize that this simple statement is a 1-dimensional version of Gauss Divergence Theorem.

Now let us see its manifestation in a very simple physical system to illustrate how it can state something significant. Consider a tube with a cross-section varying gently along its length and let some gas flow through the tube. Presumably, the density of the gas can change along the length, depending on the temperature and pressure conditions. Through any cross-section along the tube, the volume of gas flowing in a small-time Δt_1 is given by the quantity $A\Delta x_1$ where A is the area of cross-section at the location and Δx_1 is the distance that gas molecules can travel in time Δt_1 on an average. Hence the rate of mass flow through the cross-section is ρAV where $V = \Delta x_1/\Delta t_1$ is the gas velocity at that cross-section, and ρ is the density of gas at the location.

Following the 1-d statement above, we can state $\int_a^b \frac{d}{dx}(\rho AV)dx = \rho_b A_b V_b - \rho_a A_a V_a$. So far, the argument is fairly simple. By conservation of mass, the total "accumulation" inside the tube must be zero if "what comes out" matches "what goes in." However, the right-hand side $\rho_b A_b V_b - \rho_a A_a V_a$ is precisely that – what goes out minus what comes in and is zero if accumulation is zero. But now this points to something important. If the mass is conserved, then at *each location in the tube,* we must have the integrand zero, which means the "governing equation for mass conservation in this case" is $\frac{d}{dx}(\rho AV) = 0$. In this case, the situation is indeed simple, and the circus we went through still seems like a big ado about nothing. These statements' non-triviality becomes apparent when the same argument is generalized to three dimensions (or even higher dimensions).

The statement in 3-D for the divergence theorem for a vector field $\vec{V}(x, y, z)$ is –

$$\int_{\partial\Omega} \vec{V} \cdot \vec{n}\, ds = \int_{\Omega} \nabla \cdot \vec{V}\, dv$$

Here the left-hand side is integral on the boundary of domain $\partial\Omega$ (surface integral), whereas the right-hand side is integral over the domain Ω (volume integral). The right-hand side involves a specific vector calculus operation called the "divergence," giving it the name divergence theorem.

As the statement is generalized for three and higher dimensions, bookkeeping on the boundary and interior is not straightforward, for example, on spherical or ellipsoidal boundaries or, for that matter, boundaries of arbitrary shape. The most important thing is that using the divergence theorem, we can make a statement about the "interior" of the domain using "account on the boundary." This could be thought of as one of the important reasons the divergence theorem shows up in many disciplines where a governing equation is derived using conservation laws.

Further, the divergence theorem is a direct link between how the domain interacts with the surroundings at the boundary (letting flow or fluxes come in or go out at the boundary) and how the "accumulation" occurs in the interior of the domain. I must say that these statements are not "new," and to many subject matter experts may seem obvious and probably not worth mentioning with so much zest. However, my experience has been that I have missed it as a student because I was more focused on calculating the divergence correctly. Later, I found many faces in my classroom "light-up" when discussing divergence theorem in this informal manner as an instructor.

In the evolution of results leading to the divergence theorem, some key results were obtained about "vector fields" in 2-D and “line integrals.” These results are known under the title Green’s Theorem, named after George Green (1793-1841). Details of Green’s theorem and Divergence theorem can be found in vector calculus texts such as “Calculus vol 1 and vol 2” by Tom Apostol.

Emotional Inspiration:

As stated earlier, the poem was indeed motivated by the historical account of the divergence theorem's discovery, as provided in a reference given earlier. Despite teaching the theorem to students over different occasions, I had not investigated the discovery and history for quite a few years. The interested reader should read the reference pointed out earlier and related accounts available on the internet. For the poem's context, I will restate some key aspects of the discovery that appealed to me personally. The emotional reaction I had in deriving the parallels between the statement of the divergence theorem and my perspectives in the reconciliation of life-events are tied to my academic experience as a student, as an instructor, and as an individual taking a humble note of how the theorem came into place - with some twists in the history and its account.

In typical academic training, we are exposed to the Green’s theorem as a precursor to Gauss divergence theorem. However, my appreciation for this sequence completely changed when I realized that the British mathematician George Green was a mostly self-taught mathematician from Nottingshire. It seems that it is unclear how he learned the analytical techniques he used at the time. While I will leave it to historians to make authoritative statements on these, the mystery did make my revisit to Green’s theorem livelier when I read the background. Knowing that a baker’s son had discovered something significant mostly by himself and hesitated to publish it, was humbling to read. It seems that Green's work was not recognized for its significance while he was alive, and it was given the recognition due to efforts by Lord Kelvin and Stokes. It is also surprising to know that Gauss did not provide the divergence theorem's statement as used currently. The statement in Cartesian coordinate form did not appear in Gauss's work, but his ideas led to the proof.

One more piece in the history of divergence theorem that caught my attention was the third name Michael V. Ostrogadskii (1801-1861). I must admit that I did not even know this name and its association with the divergence theorem until I read the historical account. The statement of cartesian coordinate form and the associated proof is credited to Michael Ostrogadskii. Given its significance, it is puzzling to see that quite a few individuals like me would probably not know this name and its association with the divergence theorem. When I thought about this, I certainly wondered how it would feel to be in the shoes of either Mr. Green or Mr. Ostrogadskii.

Finally, I must say that the churn from the historical account of the divergence theorem did convolve with my efforts in the reconciliation of life events and their outcomes. The lack of insight about the relevance of the divergence theorem that I felt in the classroom – as a student and as an instructor, made the churn even more pronounced.

Here is a theorem that makes a statement about accumulation in the interior as a direct account of the fluxes at the domain's boundary. In contemplation, I could not avoid the parallel in my experiences where most of my inner churn seems to be directly governed by which external influences I allow to come into my inner world and affect my core and which ones I successfully avoid to defend my core.

♦

The LU Decomposition

Falling for a mathematician's stare
She said, let us set it all square
Till she asked him if their equation was solvable
He had not cared

Variables were certainly too many
They agreed they would like to eliminate as many
The dichotomy of ages did play that night
Should she go for Love or for Money?

Call of the heart was the determinant
Positive was every 'minor' and relevant
They needed some order they thought
To finish with an answer that was permanent

The day of the truth had arrived
Conclusion of sorts they derived
With passion, their eyes had turned
The night of their life they survived

She came there expecting a rose
He presented his trick with a pose
She was excited to read the letters "L U."
Alas!. He had decomposed a matrix into LU!

♠

The LU Decomposition
Mathematical Context:

LU Decomposition is a technique in solving a set of linear equations represented in matrix form. Let us consider a matrix form of linear equations $\mathbf{Ax} = \mathbf{b}$ where $\mathbf{A}$ is $n \times n$ matrix while $\mathbf{x}$ and $\mathbf{b}$ are $n \times 1$ column vectors. Let the equation be represented as below –

$$\begin{pmatrix} a_{11} & \cdots & a_{1n} \\ \vdots & \ddots & \vdots \\ a_{n1} & \cdots & a_{nn} \end{pmatrix} \begin{pmatrix} x_1 \\ \vdots \\ x_n \end{pmatrix} = \begin{pmatrix} b_1 \\ \vdots \\ b_n \end{pmatrix}$$

Solving this linear equation is equivalent to finding the inverse of the matrix $\mathbf{A}$. Now, consider the possibility that the matrix $\mathbf{A}$ can be factorized to write the equations as below-

$$\begin{bmatrix} L_{11} & 0 & 0 & 0 \\ L_{21} & L_{22} & \cdots & 0 \\ \vdots & \vdots & \ddots & \vdots \\ L_{n1} & L_{n2} & \cdots & L_{nn} \end{bmatrix} \begin{bmatrix} U_{11} & U_{12} & \cdots & U_{1n} \\ 0 & U_{22} & \cdots & U_{2n} \\ 0 & \vdots & \ddots & \vdots \\ 0 & 0 & \cdots & U_{nn} \end{bmatrix} \begin{bmatrix} x_1 \\ x_2 \\ \vdots \\ x_n \end{bmatrix} = \begin{bmatrix} b_1 \\ b_2 \\ \vdots \\ b_n \end{bmatrix}$$

The first matrix on the LHS is lower triangular (all upper triangular entries are zero). The second matrix on LHS is an upper triangular matrix (all lower triangular entries are zero), i.e., $\mathbf{A} = \mathbf{LU}$. What is the advantage if this happens? Let

$$\begin{bmatrix} U_{11} & U_{12} & \cdots & U_{1n} \\ 0 & U_{22} & \cdots & U_{2n} \\ 0 & \vdots & \ddots & \vdots \\ 0 & 0 & \cdots & U_{nn} \end{bmatrix} \begin{bmatrix} x_1 \\ x_2 \\ \vdots \\ x_n \end{bmatrix} = \begin{bmatrix} y_1 \\ y_2 \\ \vdots \\ y_n \end{bmatrix}$$

Then, the equation becomes

$$\begin{bmatrix} L_{11} & 0 & 0 & 0 \\ L_{21} & L_{22} & \cdots & 0 \\ \vdots & \vdots & \ddots & \vdots \\ L_{n1} & L_{n2} & \cdots & L_{nn} \end{bmatrix} \begin{bmatrix} y_1 \\ y_2 \\ \vdots \\ y_n \end{bmatrix} = \begin{bmatrix} b_1 \\ b_2 \\ \vdots \\ b_n \end{bmatrix}$$

This set of equations is relatively easy to solve for y_i. For example, the first equation is $L_{11}y_1 = b_1 \Rightarrow y_1 = b_1/L_{11}$. Now the second equation is $L_{21}y_1 + L_{22}y_2 = b_2$ but then y_1 is already known and hence we can easily solve for y_2. This process can continue until we get all y_i. Once all y_i are determined the remaining equations to solve are

$$\begin{bmatrix} U_{11} & U_{12} & \cdots & U_{1n} \\ 0 & U_{22} & \cdots & U_{2n} \\ 0 & \vdots & \ddots & \vdots \\ 0 & 0 & \cdots & U_{nn} \end{bmatrix} \begin{bmatrix} x_1 \\ x_2 \\ \vdots \\ x_n \end{bmatrix} = \begin{bmatrix} y_1 \\ y_2 \\ \vdots \\ y_n \end{bmatrix}$$

Here again, the last equation is $U_{nn}x_n = y_n \Rightarrow x_n = y_n/U_{nn}$ and the "backward substitution" can continue to get all x_i. Thus, if a matrix can be factorized into a lower and upper triangular matrix, the original set of equations can be solved by mere forward and backward substitutions. The conditions required for diagonal elements being non-zero etc. are omitted in this discussion to highlight the concept. What has happened here is that the elementary procedures used in solving simultaneous equations where some variables are "eliminated" by manipulations are formalized in a matrix form. For those familiar with matrix algebra, LU decomposition formalizes Gauss elimination method in a matrix form. So, one question is - can square matrices always be decomposed into LU factorization? The answer is, of course, "No."

For a start, we must concern ourselves with "invertible" square matrices that have non-zero determinants. Otherwise, the original equation is not solvable with a unique solution.

It turns out that for an invertible square matrix, a rearrangement (permutation) of equations may be necessary before getting to LU decomposition. Further, it can be shown that a square invertible matrix (after permutation) can be LU decomposed if and only if all its leading principal minors are nonzero. Principal minors are specific "determinants" of submatrices. For further details of the technique and conditions, the reader can refer to graduate texts in linear algebra.

Emotional Inspiration

The poem has a backdrop of a mathematician absorbed in solving equations to the point of losing sleep over it and his acquaintance falling in love (due to his brilliance?) who is also losing sleep over love. In my limited personal experience with mathematicians, I have found that their social and emotional intelligence appeared questionable for at least some of them. While their brilliance and acumen in mathematics were unquestionable of the highest quality, their interpersonal exchanges quite often appeared strange. I cannot say that this is categorically true of mathematicians, and no such generalization should be made. However, for the emotional reaction I had in those exchanges, I did associate it with mathematics since I had not experienced similar disconnect with individuals in other scientific disciplines until that time. I remember jokingly coming up with some individuals in graduate school with a remark directed towards particular "wannabe mathematicians." If you are a brilliant mathematician, the chance you have an attitude problem and lower emotional and social intelligence is high, but the converse is not true!

The poem seeks to exploit such disconnect in the context of the acquaintance falling in love and hoping for reciprocal love (L U as in “Love You”) from the mathematician. However, there is a major misalignment due to the statements that mean something completely different in love and in the context of mathematics.

It seems almost characteristic of mathematicians to write “LU” and not even think of “Love you”!

♦

Abstract of Abstract Algebra

Grains of the sand had found their identity
On the beach, they laid quiet and serene
Enjoying together the land, the water, and their reciprocity.

Sandstones and cliffs stared at them, aware of their gains
With beautiful formations and colors, they were adorned
However, maintained some separation each of their grains

A walk on this beach had opened my heart
The books and the pages and problems and results...
Were about to help me
Take the pieces of my tangled thoughts apart

Operations on numbers had laid the path for this breakup
Separating identity and structure
From the blend in my mind
I was now preparing to shake it up

As the soft sand was falling and slipping
Through my little fist
Some abstract algebraic notions had presented their gist

Integers, rationals, roots, and polynomials...
All were always here
With monoids and groups and rings and fields
They blended like the sandstone and formed
A mystical atmosphere

Till I questioned my 'commuting rights'
And the 'existence of identity.'
The abelian of the groups, inversion in the field,
And their relation to roots
Would not have spoken to me
About the power of abstract algebra and its enormity

Every attribute that I had so far taken for granted
Deserved scrutiny on its own
Like grains in the sandstone, its own life,
Each one had wanted

Every grain in those stones and cliffs
Had its role and reason
But the free-moving grains on the shore
Did not represent treason

All reciprocity, separations, and inversions
In my life had blended
Shaping me and my facets, it was because of them
That my identity had extended

With the setting of the evening sun,
The hour of enlightenment had arisen
The Abstract of the abstract algebra
Had then freed my mind from a prison.

♠

The Abstract of Abstract Algebra
Mathematical Context:

The poem has made subtle references to some concepts in abstract algebra. I will first briefly describe those concepts without venturing into excruciating details associated with those concepts. One can, of course, refer to graduate texts in abstract algebra for rigorous development of these concepts such as "Topics in Algebra by I. N. Herstein" or "Basic Algebra, vol-I, vol–II by Nathan Jacobson." The focus of the poem is the spirit of these developments and the way I experienced them as a student coming at them with no prior formal training in pure mathematics a couple of decades ago. The subtle emotional blend that resulted from this experience and contemplation is elaborated upon separately. Hence, I will take the liberty of describing these concepts' spirit as they appear to a curious brain, venturing in the subject as if exploring an unknown territory.

The starting point of the discussion in typical abstract algebra books is set theory and number system (integers). One of the amazing features of the development in mathematics in the twentieth century is identifying the power of abstraction. In that regard, "sets" can be thought of as the very basic structures (without life!) where the "coming together of atoms to form some things" begins. Our thinking of number system is so ingrained in us with all its rich structure due to our schooling that it requires advanced mathematics setting to question how much of it we "truly" understand in terms of "pure and complete thought." For example – a question raised earlier in the book: what exactly do we mean by one? A satisfactory answer that can be complete as a pure thought can be found in set-theoretic principles. Such a fresh outlook is necessary to isolate problems into its essentials and then make the relevant conclusions available for much wider applications, including the "development of new mathematics." Let us examine definitions of some of the basic concepts referred to-

Monoids: Monoid is a triple $(M, p, 1)$ in which M is a non-vacuous set, p is an associative binary composition (or product) in M, and 1 is an element of M such that $p(1, a) = a = p(a, 1)$

In terms of a "fresher" (someone who knows high school mathematics but is not introduced to advanced math concepts), you took a non-empty set and put a very basic demand of a structure – let there exist an operation we "may call a product" and then let there exist what we may consider "identity" so that we have relation similar to what we see in integers viz. $1 \times a = a \times 1 = a$. Our "product" operation chosen for the Monoid could very well be conventional addition in this setting. Then set of integers is a candidate for M, and what is denoted above as $p(1, a)$ is essentially $0 + a = a + 0 = a$. So, two simple examples of monoids are $(\mathbb{N}, +, 0)$, $(\mathbb{N}, \times, 1)$ where $\mathbb{N}$ is the set of natural numbers and operations defined are conventional addition and multiplication. Of course, other examples are not as simple. An example would be $M = \mathbb{Z} \times \mathbb{Z}$, which is a pair of integers (x_1, x_2) with a product defined as $(x_1, x_2)(y_1, y_2) = (x_1 y_1 + 2x_2 y_2, x_1 y_2 + x_2 y_1)$ and $1 = (1,0)$. To show that the last example is indeed, a monoid requires some work. You may see that the definition of a monoid can access some unusual structures that "behave like integers" in some respects.

This structure of a Monoid is extended further by identifying what could be called "invertible elements." An element u of a monoid M is invertible if there exists an element v in M such that $uv = 1 = vu$ where the product is understood to be the operation in M. This promotes the next structure.

Group: A non-empty set of elements G is said to form a group if in G there is defined a binary operation, called a product and denoted by ".", such that –

1. $a, b \in G$ implies that $a.b \in G$. That is – a product of two elements of G is also in G
2. $a, b, c \in G$ implies that $a.(b.c) = (a.b).c$ (associative law)
3. There exists an element $e \in G$ such that $a.e = e.a = a\ for\ all\ a \in G$.(Existence of identity)
4. For every $a \in G$ there is another element called $a^{-1} \in G$ such that $a.a^{-1} = a^{-1}.a = e$ (Invertibility)

In other words, a group is a monoid in which all elements are invertible. It should be noted that for the product operation in a group, in general, $a.b \neq b.a$. This possibility runs counter to our intuition and experience with integers but is why the richness of the structure we have in mathematical entities. For example, those familiar with linear algebra know that matrix multiplication is not commutative. When commutativity is available within a group, the group is called an Abelian group (or commutative group). Exactly what kind of structure and results become available to us due to commutativity and what we can have despite lack of commutativity would become clear only when we examine which results can be derived for groups vs. which ones are specific to abelian groups. I will leave those details to the advanced algebra textbooks.

Further enhancement of structure becomes available when we use two operations on a set. This leads to the following definition –

Associative Ring: A nonempty set R is said to be an associative ring if in R there are defined two operations, denoted by "+" and ". ", respectively, such that for all $a, b, c\ in\ R$

1. $a + b \text{ is in } R$
2. $a + b = b + a$
3. $(a + b) + c = a + (b + c)$
4. There is an element called "0" in R such that $a + 0 = a \text{ for every } a \text{ in } R$
5. There is an element denoted by $-a$ in R such that $a + (-a) = 0$
6. $a.b$ is in R
7. $a.(b.c) = (a.b).c$
8. $a.(b + c) = a.b + a.c$ and $(b + c).a = b.a + c.a$ (two distributive laws hold)

We see that a richer structure is now available. Some simple examples of a ring are integers, set of even integers, set of rational numbers, matrices with integer entries, and polynomials with integer coefficients. Out of these, the set of rational numbers has a richer structure than the others. From the set of rational numbers, a set of non-zero elements form an abelian group under multiplication. Such a ring is called a "field." In other words, we have invoked "division by non-zero elements" as an attribute in demanding a field structure.

This is not meant to be a crash course in abstract algebra, and hence the more academic discussion of these concepts is left out of the short passages above. However, in passing, I must mention that some non-trivial insights are possible only when we invoke scrutiny using similar structures. Some examples worth mentioning would be insightful results on the roots of polynomials or results in number theory. A fascinating example to which most can connect is an old problem of developing a "ruler-and-compass" construction for the trisection of a given angle. Several insightful results in abstract algebra have been invoked and used in "Galois Theory" (named after French mathematician), where the impossibility of such a construction is *proved.*

When all the excruciating details and scrutiny is set aside, and this result is looked at as a "fresher," the power of scrutiny in abstract algebra can be appreciated to some degree. The very thought that the "ruler-and-compass construction" has something to do with polynomial roots is an insight difficult to fathom as a fresher. Further, one can imagine how an indefinite number of trials may proceed without knowing that such construction is impossible for an angle's trisection. To hit the nail in the coffin – we are then presented with *proof* that definitively concludes it by showing that such a construction is not possible! For a complete experience and fascination, one must go through rigorous training in abstract algebra and then reconcile such results and the enormity of what has been accomplished. For this introduction, I would like to state a result that hopefully catches your attention and lets you observe the overwhelming emotional reaction (if there is one) to an astonishing result on polynomials.

We know from high school mathematics that a quadratic equation $ax^2 + bx + c = 0$ can be solved using the closed-form solution, which we know to be the quadratic formula. What about a cubic equation? The situation is similar, but a bit messy. Given a general cubic equation $p(x) = x^3 + a_1x^2 + a_2x + a_3 = 0$ the roots can be expressed using square roots and cube roots of rational functions of a_1, a_2, a_3. These are called Cardan's formulas. For fourth degree polynomials, by rational operations and square roots, the problem can be reduced to solving a cubic equation. Hence, a formula can be given expressing the roots in terms of combinations of radicals (surds) of rational functions of the coefficients. Now see the following celebrated theorem due to Abel (Norwegian mathematician Neils Henrik Abel) which can be proved elegantly using tools and techniques in abstract algebra –

Abel's Theorem: The general polynomial of degree $n \geq 5$ is not solvable by radicals.

I won't engage in the proof for obvious reasons but would leave you to experience your emotional reactions (if any) to this statement. To prove this result, Abel supposedly invented group theory (independent of Galois), which is extremely valuable to mathematics and many areas of physics.

Emotional Inspiration

The poem seeks to draw parallels between the spirit of abstract algebra and soul searching in the reconciliation of our personality facets. In my experience, I have perceived myself mostly as a "blend" of different characteristics which act in harmony when responding to external influences and stimuli. The situation seems remarkably like our ingrained view of the number system where we take all its rich structure for granted without being aware of the structure's elements. When looking at the sandstone, what appeals to us is the macro-scale structure and formations, which result from a specific arrangement of sub-structures emerging out of the elements represented by grains of the sand. This, to me, is just like what we perceive ourselves as ignoring the elements that make up "the blend." Only when we can question and scrutinize basic elements that make up our personality and character that true insight can be gained, and transformative growth can be enabled.

♦

Ghost of a Relation

She laid there wrapped in the white cloth
Breathless....
Waiting for the final journey
With an eerie silence
Unaware of my breath, my presence
And my adamant refusal of the moment and its essence

All of the journey had culminated
In a moment where a part of me had terminated
The other was still breathing, pumping
In harmony that was still alive and around
The belief of meaning in that void
Had still found some ground to hold and stay cemented

A feeble map from some pages in old math books
Then spoke to me
A few words of wisdom
The moments of harmony and resonance
However elegant and eternal might have felt in my heart
They formed the Kernel of a function
That related my time to her in some part

In one space alive and charming
But in its image reduced to lifeless
Was one of the most elegant of the domains in that equation
I woke up to the reality
That I was living inside the Kernel, ghost of a relation.

♠

Ghost of a Relation
Mathematical Context:

The mathematical context used in the poem is that of "Kernel of a function". For a function $f: X \to Y$, the Kernel of f is defined to be the set $Ker(f) = \{x | x \in X \text{ such that } f(x) = 0\}$. In other words, Kernel defines a subset of X where $f(x)$ vanishes. It is the *null set* of function $f(x)$. One other commonly stated definition of Kernel of a function is that it is the inverse image of zero. For example, if f is a function of set of complex numbers to set of real numbers, $f: \mathbb{C} \to \mathbb{R}$ defined as $f(z) = Im(z)$ where $Im(z)$ denotes the imaginary part of complex number z then Kernel of f is the real line embedded in the complex plane.

Emotional Inspiration

The poem is about death of a relation as experienced by the person who is not out of the relation yet.

♦

The Shock

A wave of emotions had hit me hard
Like a Tsunami in my heart
Sinking everything within me
And making me search the domain of dependence and its parts

Scrambling for survival ahead, I searched
But no characteristic curves were to be found
Everything that flowed to this point from history
Had collided and held me captive and bound

The region of influence appeared degenerate
The domain of dependence indeed brought some regret
In an instant, my heart had kinked in need
To the entire domain, I was now made to pay heed

The mathematics of that shock and its evolution
Was the genesis of an internal revolution
On paper, it depended on the initial condition
For my heartbreak, "the shock" had provided a unique rendition

Neither the domain nor the conditions
Were at any time in my control
On a trajectory chosen, what was riding
With waves and shocks towards its destiny, …. was my soul!

♠

The Shock
Mathematical Context:

The poem has a backdrop of shock phenomena modeled using partial differential equations. A brief discussion of the wave equation and a non-linear partial differential equation with a "wave-like" character is needed to provide the mathematical context. For details and rigorous development, the reader can refer to graduate texts in partial differential equations such as "Introduction to Partial Differential Equations with Applications, by E.C. Zachmanoglou and Dale W. Thoe" and "Introduction to Numerical Methods in Differential Equations by Mark H. Holmes."

First, I will state that the vibrations of a taught string held between two ends can be modeled using a partial differential equation (PDE) known as the "wave equation." The equation can be stated as below-

$$\frac{\partial^2 u}{\partial t^2} = c^2 \frac{\partial^2 u}{\partial x^2}$$

Here, constant c represents "wave speed" and is dependent on parameters such as the linear density of the string and tension in the string. The coordinate x is along the length of the string, and u represents the displacement of the string perpendicular to the nominal position of the string. This is an important second-order PDE used to describe waves as they occur in classical physics. A version of the wave equation that provides significant insights into how the solution to the second-order PDE develops based on initial conditions is the first-order wave equation(s) given below –

$$\frac{\partial u}{\partial t} - c\frac{\partial u}{\partial x} = 0 \; or \; \frac{\partial u}{\partial t} + c\frac{\partial u}{\partial x} = 0$$

If $u(x,0) = f(x)$ is given as an initial condition; a simple observation provides key insight into how the information embedded in $f(x)$ propagates through the medium. If in $x-t$ plane, we chose a line with slope $c = dx/dt$, then along such a line, we will have

$$\frac{\partial u}{\partial t} + c\frac{\partial u}{\partial x} = 0 \Rightarrow \frac{\partial u}{\partial t} + \frac{dx}{dt}\frac{\partial u}{\partial x} = 0 \Rightarrow \frac{du}{dt} = 0$$

$$along \ \frac{dx}{dt} = c$$

What this means is that the information at t=0 represented by $u(x,0) = f(x)$ is "dragged along these special lines with slope $\frac{dx}{dt} = c$ unchanged". These are the lines of propagation of information called characteristic lines. This is depicted in figure 25.

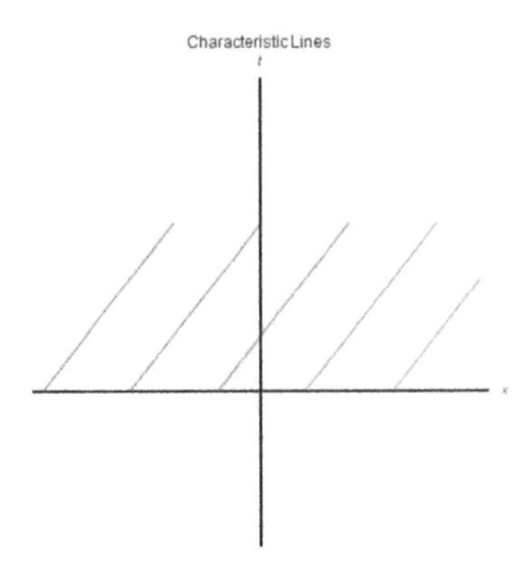

Characteristic Lines in x-t plane

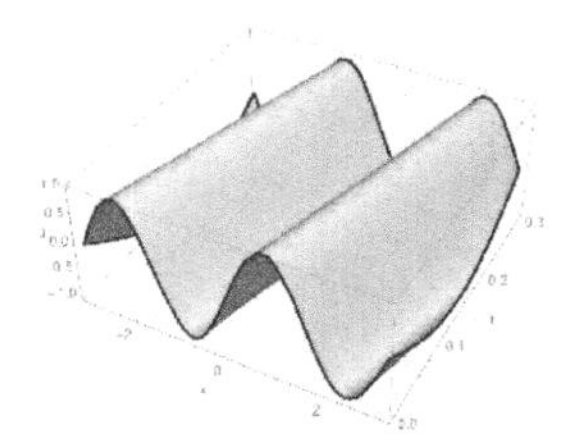

Propagation of $u(x,0) = \sin x$ in x-t along characteristic lines giving final solution $u = \sin(x - ct)$

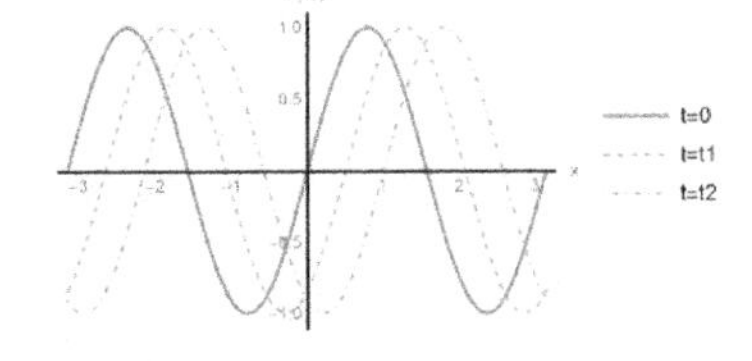

Propagation of $u(x,0) = \sin x$ viewed in $x - u$ coordinates. A wave is moving to the right giving the final solution $u = \sin(x - ct)$.

Figure 25. Illustration of how information propagates along characteristic lines and corresponding wave propagation in the first-order wave equation.

There are two sets of characteristics and information propagates in both directions at a constant speed in the solution of second-order wave equation. The corresponding plot of characteristic lines is shown in figure 26 along with regions marked as the domain of dependence and region of influence since what happens at point $u(x,t)$ *depends on domain of dependence* and then it affects the solution in *region of influence*.

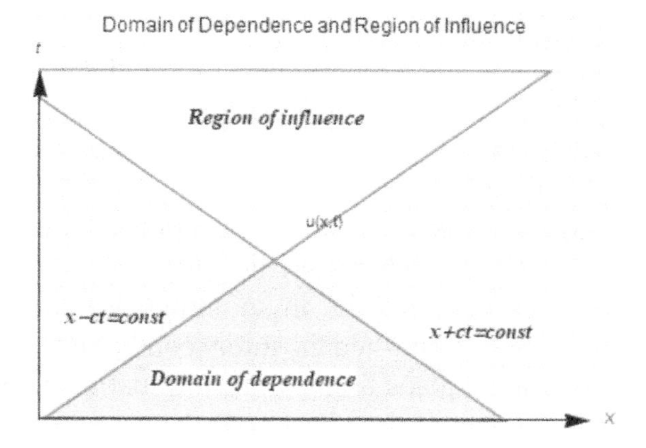

Figure 26. Two sets of characteristics with the domain of dependence and region of influence for the second-order wave equation.

The extension of this technique gives some exciting results when the governing wave equation becomes nonlinear. Such is the case for what is called "Burgers' Equation." The equation is given by

$$\frac{\partial u}{\partial t} + u\frac{\partial u}{\partial x} = \epsilon\frac{\partial^2 u}{\partial x^2}; u(x,0) = f(x)$$

Here the right-hand side represents the dissipation term, which vanishes as $\epsilon \to 0$. In this limit, the equation is very similar to the first-order wave equation except for the nonlinear term u instead of constant speed c. This equation is encountered in fluid mechanics, acoustics, gas dynamics, and modeling traffic flow! Johannes Martines Burgers studied the equation in 1948. Following the previous development, we can see that the characteristic "curves" are defined by $\frac{dx}{dt} = u(x,t)$ in this case. In other words, we no longer have straight lines along which the information propagates unless u is constant in some region. The initial condition itself can define curves and their slope along which the information propagates. In the case of constant wave speed, the slopes are fixed.

So, in the nonlinear case, part of the "wave" can move faster than the others and, in effect, can result in "colliding" behavior we refer to as a "shock," thereby forming a "kink" in the solution (discontinuous derivative) *even when the initial condition is smooth*! When dissipation is present, the shock can be avoided. In cases where dissipation is vanishingly small, and the slope of characteristic curves is such that the characteristic curves "collide" in an unfavorable manner, a shock can develop even when the initial condition is smooth. The trajectory in x-t plane for how the information will propagate beyond the shock is unclear, and other conditions (such as "entropy conditions") are invoked to obtain solutions past such a shock-event. Figure 27 illustrates two cases – one where the solution remains smooth and the other where shock tends to develop when dissipation is negligibly small.

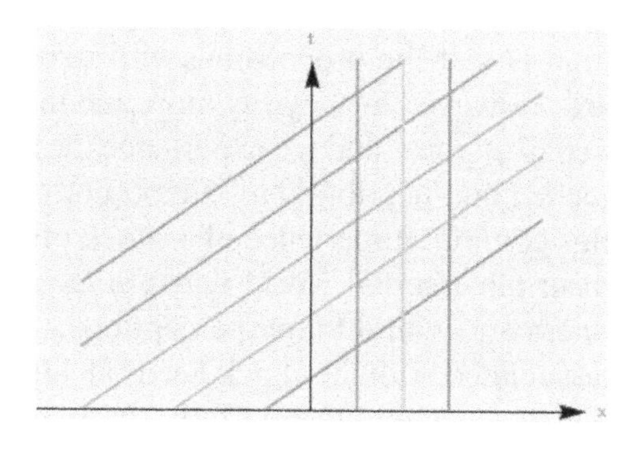

Characteristic Lines in x-t plane

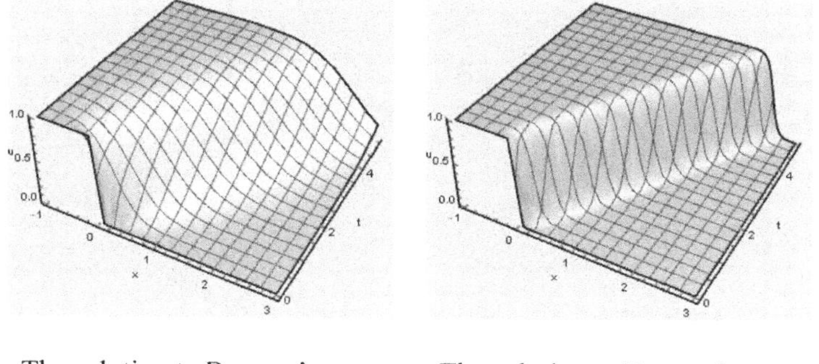

The solution to Burgers' equation remains smooth when dissipation is significant	The solution to Burgers' equation tends to develop shock with negligible dissipation.

Figure 27. Illustration of characteristic curves and shock formation in solution to Burgers' Equation.

Emotional Inspiration

The poem alludes to an emotional shock experienced in life-changing events leading to heartbreak. It seeks to draw a parallel with shock formation in nonlinear PDEs such as in Burgers' equation. It seems to me that the "shock" experienced in emotional exchanges is often related to expectations. Typically, based on smooth exchanges over a period, the expectation is that the proceedings will remain smooth going forward. However, as they say, now and then, life will throw a curveball at you – and we experience the unexpected – we are shocked and heartbroken! We do not see the kink in proceedings coming. Experience of a shock often drives a severe churn in our internal world where a lack of control and helplessness are central to our perception. All the negative energy associated with the shock needs an outlet for dissipation for us to move on meaningfully. In my experience, it is only in such instances that I have broadened my perspective and evolved as an individual.

♦

$R^2\setminus\{(0,0)\}$

With red eyes and arrhythmia
Stars of the night sky had begged for some peace
All positives of the day would play like a movie
On the backdrop of grief that would simply not cease

The beauty, purity, and sanctity of a relation
Had walked into our life like an eternal gift
Merging of our seemingly orthogonal lives
Had created 'our-2-world' causing in our hearts
A seismic kind of shift

Every vector I could find
Had in you and in me some element of its basis
Resonance of a kind had influenced our core
Challenging our soulful existence, and its homeostasis

Simple connectedness of R^2
Had come naturally to me and to you too
Every argument around had a way to collapse in the core
Since we were one and never two

What's the point?
I had wondered
Upon your reckless detachment,
On the remnants of our-2-world, I had pondered

Illusions of R^2-world could then be seen
As pieces of the leftovers, I gleaned
With the origin of the R^2-world detached
Some Cauchy sequences can't converge, it is deemed

Our-2-world with your sinister silence
Caused damage that you are yet to comprehend
The fundamental grouping of “us” has changed in a way
That neither simplicity nor closure
Can be claimed or regained

I will carry this pain for the rest of my life
With my heart punctured and sore
We remain no more “simply connected.”
And the new world is “our 2” but now without the core.

♠

$R^2\setminus\{(0,0)\}$
Mathematical Context:

The title of the poem $R^2\setminus\{(0,0)\}$ is read as R-2-minus-zero-zero and means two-dimensional real plane with origin removed. This is a specific construct that is significant in a branch of mathematics called Topology. The poem uses some references to concepts in Topology and vector spaces metaphorically. I will prefer to introduce the basic concepts that are sufficient to understand the terminology and the metaphorical usage in the poem. This commentary on mathematical context is admittedly longer than I would have liked to write. However, I believe that the reader always has the option to skip it, and those interested can attend to the details.

By R^2 is meant a pair of real numbers (r_1, r_2) with certain operations commensurate with what is called a "Vector Space." A formal definition of vector space is as below. A vector space consists of –

1. A field F of scalars. (In our case, this is a field of real numbers)
2. A set V of objects called vectors
3. A rule (or operation) called vector addition which associates with each pair of vectors α, β in V a vector $\alpha + \beta$ in V, called the sum of α and β, in such a way that
   a. The addition is commutative, $\alpha + \beta = \beta + \alpha$
   b. The addition is associative, $\alpha + (\beta + \gamma) = (\alpha + \beta) + \gamma$
   c. There is a unique vector 0 in V called the zero vector such that $\alpha + 0 = \alpha$ for all α in V.
   d. For each vector α in V there is a unique vector $-\alpha$ in V such that $\alpha + (-\alpha) = 0$

4. A rule (or operation) called scalar multiplication, which associates with each scalar $c \ in \ F$ and a $vector \ \alpha \ in \ V$ a vector $c\alpha \ in \ V$ called the product of $c \ and \ \alpha$ in such a way that
   a. $1.\alpha = \alpha$ for $every \ \alpha \ in \ V$
   b. $(c_1c_2)\alpha = c_1(c_2\alpha)$
   c. $c(\alpha + \beta) = c\alpha + c\beta$
   d. $(c_1 + c_2)\alpha = c_1\alpha + c_2\alpha$

It is clear that conventional 2-dimensional vectors (R^2) and 3-dimensional vectors (R^3) with real numbers representing their components are vector spaces. The point of the above definition is that the structure available to us in these spaces $R^2, R^3 \ or \ R^n$ can be made available in other mathematical entities as well for some insightful analysis as long as the requirements in the above definition are met, e.g., matrices can be considered vector spaces, polynomials with real coefficients can also be considered as a vector space, set of continuous functions on [0,1] is a vector space when operations on functions are meaningfully defined, stress at a point in a solid can be modeled as an operator (linear function) on vector space R^3 and, in turn, itself be treated as an element of another vector space. For R^2 the two vectors $e_1 = (1,0) \ and \ e_2 = (0,1)$ are considered (orthogonal) basis vectors since all vectors in R^2 can be written as a linear combination of $e_1 \ and \ e_2$. The notion of orthogonality in a vector space relies on another formal and abstract definition of what is commonly known as a "dot product." The "x-axis (X)" is a space spanned by $(1,0)$, and "y-axis (Y)" is space spanned by (0,1), and each $X \ and \ (or) \ Y$ are in their own right "vector spaces." These two orthogonal spaces have "united" (Product space $X \times Y$) to form what we call R^2 (referred to in the poem as $R^2 \ world$)

The second key reference in the poem requires a brief commentary about what is called Topological Spaces. We will look at two more definitions

Topology: A topology on a set X is a collection Ω of subsets of X (often called open sets) having the following properties

1. $Empty\ set\ \phi\ and\ X$ are is in Ω
2. A union of elements of any subcollection of Ω is in Ω.
3. The intersection of the elements of any finite subcollection of Ω is in Ω

Topological Space: A set X for which topology Ω has been specified is called a topological space.

Some commonly available examples of topological spaces are real line R with topology defined by a collection of open sets (think of a collection of open intervals) on the real line, or similarly R^2 with topology defined by sets that are "R^2-open" (Think of a collection of open disks. The open unit disk is set of all points $(x, y) with\ x^2 + y^2 < 1$). What is the point of such a definition? Well, that will take some course work to explain. An oversimplified answer is that topology provides a notion of "neighborhood" of an element in X. Once we start thinking about "neighborhoods" and "closeness," we can hope to get some calculus-like features available on entities which otherwise wouldn't fit the bill. Fast forward a few pages in the graduate text in topology, and you see a definition of continuous map $f: X \to Y$ between two topological spaces to be a map where "inverse image of an open set in Y under f is an open set in X." I will just let the curiosity sit with you without explaining this definition. A reader can get more formal exposure in graduate texts such as in "Topology, A First Course by James R. Munkres." What has happened here is that all our notion of continuity in calculus taking limits and saying $\lim_{x \to a} f(x) = f(a)$, dealing with "infinitesimals" and all that has been stripped to its bare essentials and it is identified that if we can meaningfully define "neighborhoods" in a set, then we can define "continuity of mappings" between sets, thereby making the notion of "continuity" available for many structures outside of R^n, for example, on a set of functions.

Once the notion of "neighborhood" is available, significant other developments are undertaken in topology, and then we come to the notion of "connectedness." Our intuitive notion that Australia is not "connected" by land with Africa finds its bare essential elements identified in topological definition of connectedness. A topological space is "separated" if the space X can be written as a union of two disjoint nonempty open sets. The space X is said to be connected if there does not exist a separation of X. A space X is "path connected" if for every pair of points x, y in X, we can have a continuous map (path) $f: [0,1] \to X$ where $f(0) = x$ and $f(1) = y$. Now comes a notion called "simply connected." Now that we have a notion of "path" in a topological space, I will take the liberty to have a "loop" in topological space as a path that starts and ends at the same point (not self-intersecting). If we can "continuously" deform (have a continuous parametric map) this path staying in the topological space and collapse it in one point, then the topological space is simply connected. A unit disk in R^2 is simply connected since any "loop" can be deformed continuously and collapsed into one point but an annulus defined by $\{All\ (x, y) such\ that\ 1 < \sqrt{x^2 + y^2} < 2\}$ is not simply connected, for you can't collapse a circle of radius 1.5 centered at the origin (which lies in this topological space) into one point. Another example of a space that is connected but not simply connected is R^2 with origin removed i.e. $R^2 \backslash \{(0,0)\}$. R^2 By itself is simply connected, but with the removal of one point, it becomes not simply connected because a circle with a center at the origin can't be collapsed into one point by continuous "deformations." In this regard, the annular disk described earlier is topologically similar to $R^2\backslash\{(0,0)\}$. It is interesting to note that this is not the case with R^3. When you remove the origin, $R^3\backslash\{(0,0,0)\}$ is still simply connected, just like a spherical surface. Thus, there is a basic character of the topological space captured by examining simple connectedness. See figure 28.

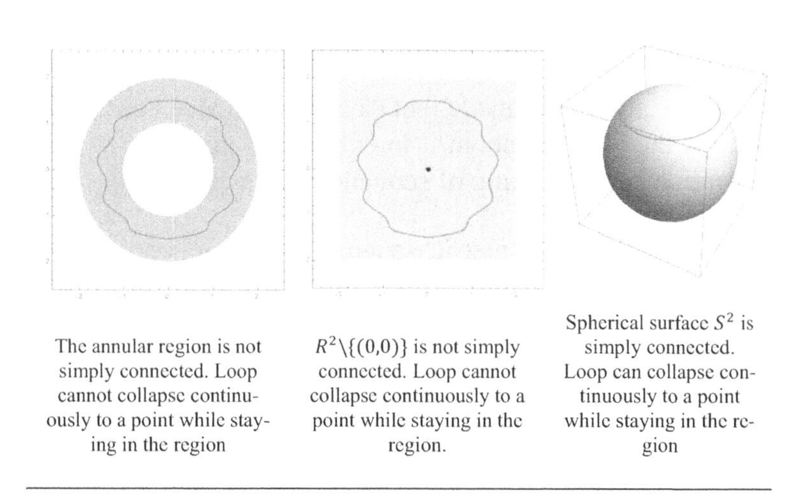

The annular region is not simply connected. Loop cannot collapse continuously to a point while staying in the region

$R^2\backslash\{(0,0)\}$ is not simply connected. Loop cannot collapse continuously to a point while staying in the region.

Spherical surface S^2 is simply connected. Loop can collapse continuously to a point while staying in the region

Figure 28. Illustration of simple connectedness

Removal of origin fundamentally alters R^2 in terms of connectedness. This is characterized in topology by a notion called the fundamental group of the topological space. Removal of one point from R^2 changes it in a very fundamental manner and its fundamental group changes. Although at different locations in $R^2\backslash\{(0,0)\}$, local neighborhoods are still $R^2 - like$, removal of one point changes its fundamental character.

There is also a reference to Cauchy sequences in the poem. I feel compelled to write a couple of lines about that reference. A formal definition of Cauchy sequence in a "metric space" is given below. A "metric space" is a topological space where some notion of "distance between two points" $d(x, y)$ is defined, e.g., in R^2,

$$d(A, B) = \sqrt{(x_a - x_b)^2 + (y_a - y_b)^2}.$$

Cauchy Sequence: A sequence $\{p_n\}$ in a metric space X is said to be a Cauchy sequence if, for every $\epsilon > 0$, there is an integer N such that $d(p_n, p_m) < \epsilon$ if $n, m \geq N$.

When a statement is made that Cauchy sequence converges, what is the big deal about it in contrast to invoking a usual definition of converging of sequences such as below? –

A sequence $\{a_n\}$ in metric space X is said to converge if there is a point P such that for every $\epsilon > 0$, there is an integer N such that $d(a_n, P) < \epsilon$ if $n > N$.

The second definition is tied to "object P" (possibly outside of the world in which the sequence "lives") while a statement that Cauchy sequence converges is entirely within the space of interest. A subtle point indeed, but worth a separate statement, that too with a name associated being one of the heavyweights in the field – Cauchy! I had completely missed this subtlety in my first encounter with the definition until I was faced with the construct $R^2 \backslash \{(0,0)\}$ and sequence $p_n = \left(\frac{1}{n}, 0\right)$. Cauchy sequences give rise to the notion of "completeness." Fields, where all Cauchy sequences converge, are not missing any numbers. In the "fresher" language, there are no "holes" in the space if every Cauchy sequence is deemed convergent.

Emotional Inspiration

The poem engages in the experience of meeting a "soulmate" and then experiencing a heartbreak. It seeks to draw the parallel between losing someone or something from the "inner circle" and removal of the origin in R^2 both of which fundamentally change the character of the "world we are in."

Some reading on how people experience harmony and convergence when they meet their "soulmate" or when they are immersed in work about which they are naturally passionate, and how people experience heartbreak shows that all of these fundamentally shake a person's core. In many cases, a heartbreak renders them dysfunctional till they recover from it. Comparisons can be found where people experiencing heartbreaks can show behaviors like withdrawal symptoms of addicts. While I am not an expert in psychology, I can still connect to the relevance of the associated loss, grief, and the nature of fundamental change associated with an event like meeting a "soulmate" or experiencing a heartbreak. The only qualification required for that is being human with a sensitive mind.

To describe how a heartbreak experience changes something fundamentally in the core, it has provoked many writings and art forms over centuries. However, the imagery provided by $R^2\backslash\{(0,0)\}$ and the associated change of the fundamental character of the topological space was the first unexpected candidate in this list for me.

The use of "our-2-world" to emphasize the parallel with "R^2 *world*", in the poem, is intentional. The last stanza refers to "our-2" as an indication of version-2 of relation after the heartbreak – whatever that version may be. It is often claimed that it is impossible to move on from a heartbreak until you have openly and fully accepted the new reality and how things have changed fundamentally in your perception. ♦

A Hausdorff Space

Like singleton points
I saw us scattered in each of our own early lives
Unaware of intervals, domains, and connections
And yet to discover a place in our hearts
Where the truth resides.

As sets, neighborhoods, and connections
Took shape on the pages of the book in my hand
Topological mysteries of my thought and mind
Appeared so pure and grand!

All of a sudden, with these books, I had wandered
In the barren land of sets without life
Early chapters of topology had shown
Ways of tearing the elements of intuition
With a surgical knife

In the mysterious space of love
Every neighborhood I could draw had me and you
Not only were we 'path-connected,'
It was like having two souls merged with an invisible glue!

Such a construct did not exist in Topological spaces I knew
Where they synthesized even complex of the manifolds
I was convinced that it was because,
Beyond the worldly matters
True meaning and purpose, this relation holds!

It was only when I saw the
Cantor set breaking into its self-similar parts
And space-filling curves challenging my notion of 'smart.'
That while your departure from my proximity
Had shaken my core
The hurt and the longing I could still reconcile in my heart.

Realizing the continuum of 'the soul' was a good start
I had now the courage to pick up my part
Relations and true connections, with time, do morph
Even this pure space of heart affairs is, after all, Hausdorff!

♠

A Hausdorff Space Mathematical Context:

Hausdorff space is a topological concept named after a German mathematician Felix Hausdorff, one of the founders of modern Topology. In the mathematical context for the previous poem $R^2\backslash\{(0,0)\}$, there was a brief discussion of Topological spaces and an introduction to some related concepts. I will state the definition of Topological space here again for the sake of completion and then discuss Hausdorff condition followed by a manifold, Cantor set, and space-filling curves. In the academic development of topology, this sequence would not be considered coherent, but for providing the poem's context, this would make more sense, in my opinion.

Topology: A topology on a set X is a collection Ω of subsets of X (often referred to as open sets) having the following properties –

1. $Empty\ set\ \phi\ and\ X$ are in Ω
2. A union of elements of any subcollection of Ω is in Ω.
3. The intersection of the elements of any finite subcollection of Ω is in Ω

Topological Space: A set X for which topology Ω has been specified is called a topological space.

Some common examples of topological spaces were mentioned earlier, such as R^n, the n-tuple of real numbers under Euclidean measure of distance. It will be worthwhile this time to examine some non-trivial examples of topological spaces. Consider two-dimensional plane R^2. The "open sets" are now defined as a different collection rather than the usual collection of "open disks." Let a set Ω_1 consist of $\emptyset$ the entire plane and compliments of a finite number of points. This collection of sets declared as "open sets" is a topology, i.e., only closed sets are a finite number of points. This combination, i.e., two- dimensional plane with Ω_1 can be seen to satisfy the requirements in the definition of a topological space. Now equipped with this topology, we can see some strange behaviors in "neighborhoods." One observation is that given any two points x, y on the plane, we can not find two open sets V_1 *and* V_2 such that $x \in V_1, y \in V2$ *and* $V_1 \cap V_2 = \emptyset$.

In the language of the "fresher,," in this topology, we can't find neighborhoods for x *and* y such that the two neighborhoods, one containing each, are "separated" from each other! An open set containing x and an open set containing y will always have some region in common. This is counter to our intuition about neighborhoods founded in our experience in real spaces and the Euclidean metric. It is natural to think that this is a pathological construct highlighting how weird an abstraction like topological space can become. However, it turns out that such topological spaces have some use in studying polynomial equations in algebraic geometry. I am not qualified to discuss those applications, and such a discussion is probably not prudent for this brief introduction. This leads to the following definition for what is called a Hausdorff space.

Hausdorff Space: A topological space X is called a Hausdorff space if for each pair x_1, x_2 of distinct points of X, there exist neighborhoods U_1 and U_2 of x_1 and x_2, respectively, that are disjoint.

Such a topological space is also called T_2 space. It turns out that Hausdorff originally introduced this condition as an axiom in topology. Introducing it as an axiom rather than a class of topological spaces has always made more sense to me as a student. This condition deserves a separate mention, and identification as a class of topological spaces is itself worth a pause, in my opinion. I remember after reading the definition above and wondering before bedtime as a student if taking a non-Hausdorff topological space as an object of attention and investing time in its mathematical scrutiny was a sign of deviating from "normality" (in the sense of normal human behavior, not "normal topological space"!). Figure 29 illustrates the notion of a Hausdorff Space.

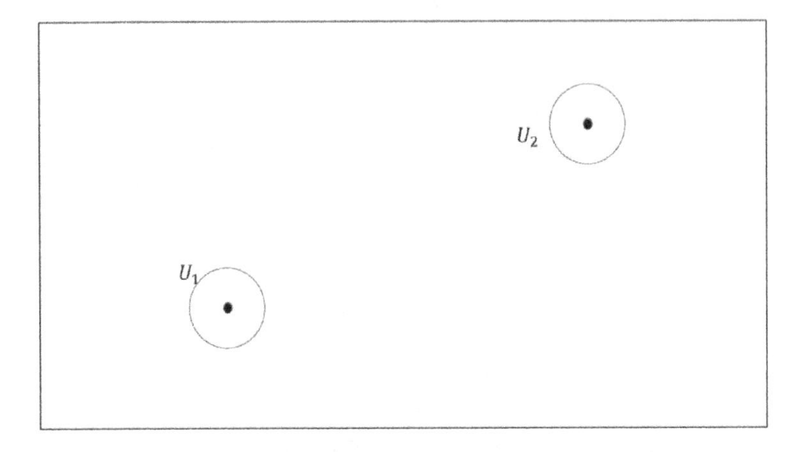

Figure 29. Illustration of Hausdorff Condition

There are three more references in the poem which are worth mentioning. The terms are "manifold," "Cantor set," and a "space-filling curve." All three concepts have fascinated me personally and, in some sense, more than the definition of Hausdorff space.

Manifold: Manifold is a topological space that resembles Euclidean space locally near each point. For example, a spherical surface is a two-dimensional manifold since, in the neighborhood of each point, it is like R^2. One can think of how the surrounding is like a plane at each location on earth while the earth itself is round. Of course, there are many other interesting examples of manifolds one can think of, such as a set of zeros of polynomial functions of multiple variables, e.g., zeros of $f(x,y) = ax^2 + by^2 - c$ can be conic sections, which are 1-dimensional manifolds.

Cantor Set: The Cantor set is a special set named after German Mathematician Georg Cantor, on a line segment with some remarkable deep properties. Through the consideration of this set, Cantor and others laid the foundation for modern point set topology. The construction of Cantor set proceeds as follows –

Let E_0 be the unit interval [0,1]. Remove segment $\left(\frac{1}{3}, \frac{2}{3}\right)$ and let E_1 be the union of intervals

$$E_1 = \left[0, \frac{1}{3}\right] \cup \left[\frac{2}{3}, 1\right]$$

Remove the middle thirds of these intervals, and let E_2 be the union of intervals

$$E_2 = \left[0, \frac{1}{9}\right] \cup \left[\frac{2}{9}, \frac{3}{9}\right] \cup \left[\frac{6}{9}, \frac{7}{9}\right] \cup \left[\frac{8}{9}, 1\right]$$

Continuing this way, we obtain a sequence of sets (which are compact) such that

(a) $E_1 \supset E_2 \supset E_3 \supset \cdots$;
(b) E_n is the union of 2^n intervals each of length 3^{-n}

The set

$$P = \bigcap_{n=1}^{\infty} E_n$$

It is called the Cantor Set. It can be shown that P is non-empty. Further, the following can be claimed –

1. P is totally disconnected (by topological definition of connectedness).
2. P is a compact set. (closed and bounded)
3. $End\ points\ of\ each\ E_n$ are in P
4. Every point of P is a limit point. This means – pick any point $x \in P$ and pick any neighborhood of x, and you will find some point $y \in P, y \neq x$ in that neighborhood.
5. P is uncountable but of measure zero, i.e., negligibly small "size" but uncountably infinite. (for a brief discussion of countability and measure, see the discussion following "Differentiation under the Integral sign")

In the language of a "fresher," the last of the above statements claiming uncountability means that "there are as many points left in P as there were, to begin with, because both [0,1] and P are uncountably infinite! One can construct a map from P *onto* [0,1] – in the language of analysis, a surjective map! Cantor set is a prototype of a *fractal*.

Rendition of similar construction in higher dimensions gives similar fascinating sets. Illustration in 3D is shown in figure 30.

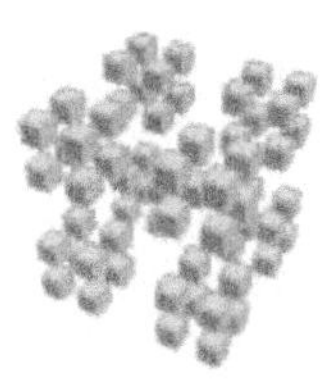

Figure 30. Illustration of Cantor set construction in 3D up to E_3. (Ref: Code from Wolfram Mathematica documentation)

Peano Space-Filling Curve: This is a special construct in the topology that challenges our intuitive notion of continuity and "size" of sets. Several such fascinating constructs can be found in graduate texts in topology. Some examples would be - a function discontinuous everywhere, a continuous function that is differentiable nowhere, etc. The space-filling curve is a continuous map of interval $I = [0,1]$ to unit square $I \times I$. Such a curve is generated recursively by introducing "kinks" and continuing indefinitely (similar to how Cantor set was generated). This process is illustrated in figure 31. We can have a curve fill-up the "space" implies in the language of the "fresher" that there are as many points in the interval I as there are in the unit square! Thus, there appear to be at least "two types of infinities" – one that is "countable infinite," like what we encountered in integers or rational numbers and the second encountered in an interval on the real line.

The thought that infinities can come in different sizes is a great one to engage in if you are having trouble sleeping someday. To try and outsmart this one or absorbing it too deeply is quite daunting and could very well give you your first encounter with a psychological phenomenon called "learned helplessness." After that, if you get up exhausted the next morning, you can lighten up thinking of the 1995 Pixar film Toy Story with Buzz Lightyear saying, "To infinity...and beyond" ...just ask "Hey, but which infinity?"

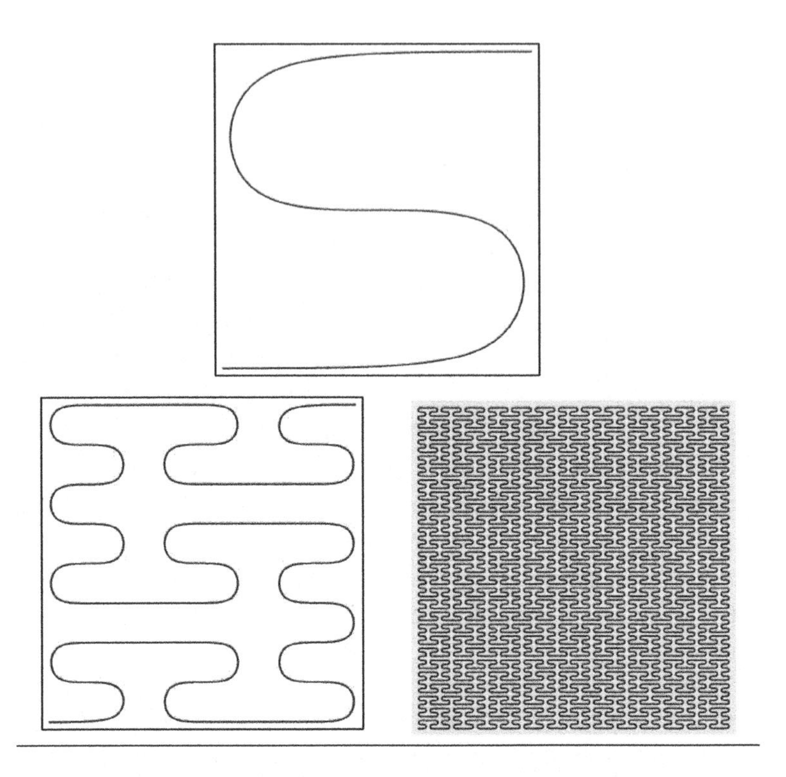

Figure 31. Illustration of steps in constructing Peano Space-Filling Curve recursively. The process above is to be continued indefinitely to fill the square. (Ref: Code from Wolfram Mathematica documentation)

The poem starts with revisiting the days of innocent growth. It compares the curiosity in exploring our inner world with the "fresher" gaining experience through an introduction to topology out of curiosity.

Like singleton points
I saw us scattered in each of our own early lives
Unaware of intervals, domains, and connections
And yet to discover a place in our hearts
Where the truth resides.

As sets, neighborhoods, and connections
Took shape on the pages of the book in my hand
Topological mysteries of my thought and mind
Appeared so pure and grand!

Then of course, comes the shock and awe of experiencing elements of intuition taken apart for scrutiny and the quest starting with sets and building the topological structure "ground up"!

All of a sudden, with these books, I had wandered
In the barren land of sets without life
Early chapters of topology had shown
Ways of tearing the elements of intuition
With a surgical knife

This is followed by immersing oneself in the intricacies of the subject matter just as one lets the mind go into free fall when "falling" in love –

In the mysterious space of love
Every neighborhood I could draw had me and you
Not only were we 'path-connected,'
It was like having two souls merged with an invisible glue!

Such a construct did not exist in Topological spaces I knew
Where they synthesized even complex of the manifolds
I was convinced that it was because,
Beyond the worldly matters
True meaning and purpose, this relation holds!

Then comes the maturing process with painful experiences such as separation from a loved one or realizing the loss of connection with someone near and dear and subsequent desperation in reconciliation –

It was only when I saw
The Cantor set breaking into its self-similar parts
And space-filling curves challenging my notion of 'smart.'
That while your departure from my proximity
Had shaken my core
The hurt and the longing I could still reconcile in my heart.

The last stanza provides a change of perspective. Often when we think of someone as being in the "inner circle" or being a "soulmate," we have experienced perfect harmony of thoughts, emotions, and exchanges. It is often reported by people having "met their soulmates" that they instantly find the experience to be like "being home" or "two bodies, one soul." I am not an expert in relationships; however, it is also found that relations evolve and change their form with time. Over a period, even those who are "soulmates" seem to seek their individual space – some while staying in harmony while some others through a painful separation. The poem attempts to draw the parallel between each person seeking individual space and Hausdorff's separation axiom. It comes as a revelation that even soulmates have some inner core reserved for themselves.

Realizing the continuum of 'the soul' was a good start
I had now the courage to pick up my part
Relations and true connections, with time, do morph
Even this pure space of heart affairs is, after all, Hausdorff!

♦

The Genus of a Manifold

Like a craftsman
I build my core, chipping one facet at a time
With mathematical precision, I sharpen
To remove emotions as if swaying with them
Would be a crime

I have been rebuilding myself
To asymptotically approximate my 'self'
With a simplicial complex
Removing possibilities of illusions
Arising out of maps and morphs
Now every perception of the external,
Has at the root, some simplex.

With structure came -
Categorization of the free-flowing
Braking pictures into pieces for knowing
Separating intuition, emotions, and logic like winnowing

Like a triangulated manifold
Life has been mapped
For characterizations, projections, paths, and predictions,
In analysis and equations, all have been nicely wrapped

It is only now that I have arrived
At a juncture to know how my self has all through survived
In all of my journey,
Like genus of a manifold,

The character was dictated by extremes,
Not by regression and trends
Structured projections gave me increments
While life was decided by a few singular bends!

♠

The Genus of a Manifold
Mathematical Context:

The genus of a manifold is a concept from topology. It is used to represent a certain character of the orientable surface. The concept of a manifold was discussed in the last poem's mathematical context, “A Hausdorff Space.” I will repeat it here for completeness and proceed to introduce other terms used in the poem.

Manifold: Manifold is a topological space that resembles Euclidean space locally near each point. Some simple examples of manifolds were discussed earlier.

Genus: For an orientable connected surface (2-manifold), its genus is an integer representing a maximum number of cuttings along non-intersecting closed simple curves without rendering the resulting manifold disconnected. It is equal to the number of handles on it. In layman terms, it is the number of “holes” that an object has. For example, a sphere S^2 is a surface of genus-zero, while a torus is a surface of genus 1. Figure 32 depicts a surface with a different value of the genus. The Genus of a surface fundamentally characterizes its topological structure. For example, a coffee mug and torus both are topologically equivalent and have genus 1.

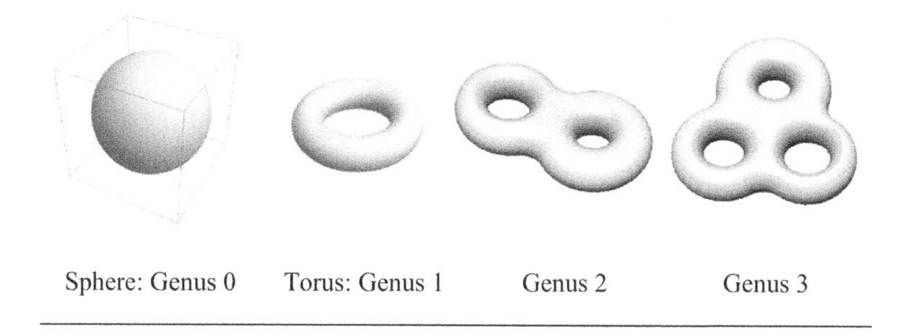

Figure 32. Depiction of surfaces with different values of genus.

I must emphasize that the genus of a manifold characterizes the fundamental character of the manifold. Loosely speaking (layman terms), two manifolds with the same genus can be mapped to each other through "continuous deformations." This is impossible if the two manifolds have different genus. For example, a coffee mug and torus both are genus 1, and one can be "deformed" to acquire the other shape; such is not the case for the manifold of genus one and manifold of genus 2.

Simplicial complex: In topology, a simplex (plural simplices) is a generalization of the notion of a triangle or tetrahedron. The 0-simplex is a point, 1-simplex is a segment, 2-simplex is a triangle, 3-simplex is a tetrahedron, and this is continued to higher dimensions. Specifically, a $k-simplex$ is a k −dimensional prototype, which is the convex hull of its $k+1$ vertices.

A simplicial complex is a set consisting of simplices. Figure 33 illustrates the concept of a simplicial complex rendered in 3D.

Triangulated manifold: It is interesting mathematically and for computational modeling, to note that region of a manifold can be "approximately represented" by a simplicial complex. When the entire manifold is represented by relevant simplicial complex, the manifold is considered "triangulated." Figure 33 shows an example of a triangulated manifold in 3D, but the concept extends this notion to higher dimensions.

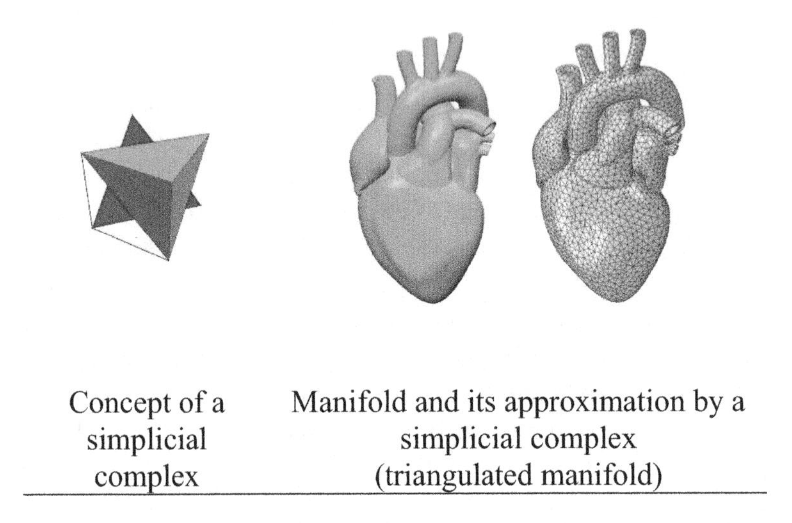

Figure 33. Illustration of simplicial complex and a triangulated manifold. (Figure courtesy of N. Manthalkar)

Emotional Inspiration:

I find it difficult to write the emotional inspiration behind this poem, and I am tempted to leave it to the poem's expression. Through my formative years, especially through academic training in mathematics and physical sciences, I have found that rational thinking took center stage. It slowly became ingrained in the thought process to revere a rational and structured approach towards problems of any kind over reliance on emotions. This was true of both academic as well as non-academic problems. My brief exposure to mathematicians, their thinking, as well as fortunate encounters with people of significant stature in engineering and business, has made me think about dominating factors that shape our lives. One of the inclinations I developed through my training as a mathematics and science student was to examine the trends and projections to re-align expectations and outlook for the future. However, I must admit that this approach often worked on "increments" but failed to give a holistic view. Most of the significant changes that have shaped my life and growth as a person seem to come from singular events that I have perceived to be rare – events like a bifurcation point in life! Just like encountering a "hole" changes the manifold's fundamental character "irreversibly," my encounter with these singular events have dominated my evolution to the person I am today. I find this reconciliation perplexing and in conflict with my training that relied on a rational and structured approach that focused on trends and projections.

♦

Details Are Left to the Reader as an Exercise

Confluence of contradictions
Had taken a fall
On the chilly banks of Niagara
While in my heart
The bright snow and its reflection
Had shown the signs of an impending brawl

Through my triple-fat-goose
The chill inside had challenged the snow
When the probability, the tosses, and transitions of my life
Had flashed and splashed on that rock at the bottom
Presenting my past, present, and future
Scattering the droplets and disrupting the flow

My effort had not led to success
My failure has not resulted in distress
What runs in my veins today, I thought,
Has its color and character
For inexplicable reasons,
Which my heart was then forced to reassess

I had been transitioning
Within accessible states
Recurrent, transient, and some sets closed
Pieces of me were left there, scattered along the way
Will they ever reunite in the future?
Was the question the maid of the mist had then posed

The canonical form of my p-matrix
Had left some unfilled places
The apparent transitions
And their probabilities, then I knew
Carried with them my DNA and illusion of its traces

Like the droplets of Niagara floating on the wind
And feathers of a bird fallen from the wing
My pieces and traces had taken a flight for migration
While some were still stuck
In their invariant distribution

The spirit inside of which
This moment's glory is supposed to be the spark of
Screamed at me louder than the roar of the Niagara
That my evolution in time was never Markov
With shaken faith, to myself, I had tried to talk
Was my tomorrow a function or a functional?
That was going to dictate my walk

The polar opposites had resided inside of me all along
The path of Nirvana now
Is to free from the shackles of Karma
So that my next jump is Markov

The yellow books had been preparing me
For this all these years
With a key to my rise
The rest of it cannot be made precise
Because details are left to the reader as an exercise.

♠

Details Are Left to the Reader as an Exercise Mathematical Context:

The mathematical context for this poem is Markov Chains in the theory of probability and statistics. Most introductory treatment of probability starts with an analysis of events described as independent trials, e.g., flipping a coin. In the theory of Markov chains, we consider the simplest generalization that the probability of the trial's outcome is dependent *directly and only on* the outcome of directly preceding trial. In this framework, we continue the trials, and the system of interest occupies certain states in each trial. For instance, if we are tossing two coins, there are four possible states that the system can be in which are $\{Head-Head, Head-Tail, Tail-Head, Tail-Tail\}$. If we study the sequence of tossing two coins, one can think of the system as occupying one of the four states. If the coins are biased, the probabilities associated with each state are not the same. In this particular case, there is no reason to think that the next toss will somehow depend on the previous toss and the trials would be considered independent. However, there can be situations where the next outcome depends on the current state. Markov chains represent such transitions.

It is instructive to see an example where all this formalism plays out. To have fun with the description while sketching the formalism, I will make up a matrix for two states in which promiscuous Bob's heart can be in a given month $S = \{In\ love, heart\ broken\} = \{0,1\}$. Let the probability that Bob experiences heartbreak in love be α. Hence, the probability that he remains in love while in love is $1-\alpha$. Let the probability that Bob falls in love when heartbroken be β. Hence the probability that Bob remains heartbroken when his heart is broken is $1-\beta$. Since α and β represent probabilities, we must have both $\alpha, \beta \in [0,1]$ and let $0 < \alpha + \beta < 2$. In this case, the probabilities of transition can be represented by what is called a p-matrix for Bob's heart -

$$P = \begin{bmatrix} 1-\alpha & \alpha \\ \beta & 1-\beta \end{bmatrix}$$

Here the entry $p_{12} = \alpha$ represents the probability of transition from state 1 to state 2 (i.e., $0 \rightarrow 1$). It is customary to represent such a system with a Markov chain diagram such as the one below –

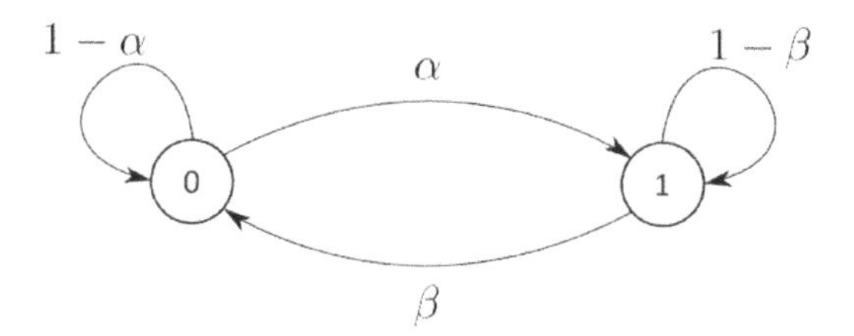

Figure 34. Two state Markov Chain

In January, let the probability distribution for the state of Bob's heart be $v = [a, 1-a]; a \in [0,1]$, i.e., probability that Bob is in love in January is a, and the probability that he is heartbroken in January is $1-a$. After sufficiently many affairs, what can be said about the state of Bob's heart?

For example, if in January the distribution is $[a, 1-a]$ then since Bob transitions within a month, in February, the probability distribution for the state of his heart is

$$v_1 = v.P = [a \quad 1-a] \begin{bmatrix} 1-\alpha & \alpha \\ \beta & 1-\beta \end{bmatrix}$$

In March $v_2 = v.P^2$ *and so on.* After n affairs (transitions), the probability distribution will be $v_n = v.P^n$. In this particular case, after sufficiently many affairs ($n \to \infty$), it can be shown using some Algebra and calculus that $v_\infty = \left[\frac{\beta}{\alpha+\beta}, \frac{\alpha}{\alpha+\beta}\right]$. *Details are left to the reader as an exercise – yes, like those Springer yellow math books!* This suggests that after "many-many affairs," the state of Bob's heart will have reached the so-called "limiting" distribution of this Markov chain given by v_∞ where probability that he is in love is $\beta/(\alpha+\beta)$ and the probability that he is heartbroken is $\alpha/(\alpha+\beta)$. Just for fun, you may want to read these probability fractions using the description of α *and* β instead of reading Greek letters. Note that if Bob starts with this distribution and goes through a transition on a beach in Hawaii, the next distribution is still v_∞ i.e $v_\infty . P = v_\infty$ (can be verified by matrix multiplication). This distribution satisfying the equation $v.P = v$ is called the *stationary or invariant distribution* for the given Markov chain since further transitions from this distribution do not change the distribution. While we are at it, let us give Bob a lesson in Morality using Markov Chains. Once Bob's transition matrix is defined, regardless of the starting distribution, he is destined to reach his invariant distribution in the long run. So, he better finds the love of his life and stops being promiscuous!

The reader can get formal and rigorous discussion in texts such as "An Introduction to Probability Theory and its Applications" by William Feller. Below, the outline of the framework relevant to the poem is described.

To examine the formal definition of a Markov chain, we may consider a set of possible outcomes being given -

$$E_1, E_2, \ldots (finite\ or\ infinite)$$

To every pair (E_j, E_k) there corresponds a conditional probability p_{jk}; given that E_j has occurred in some trial, the probability that E_k occurs in the next trial is p_{jk}. In addition to the p_{jk} we must also be given probability a_k of the outcome E_k at the initial trial (like distribution given for Bob in January in the prior example). Considering the initial trial numbered zero if the sequence of occurrence of states is $E_{j_0}, E_{j_1}, \ldots, E_{j_n}$ the associated probability of this occurrence is

$$P\left(E_{j_0}, E_{j_1}, \ldots, E_{j_n}\right) = a_{j_0} p_{j_0 j_1} p_{j_1 j_2} \cdots p_{j_{n-1} j_{n-2}} p_{j_{n-1} j_n}$$

Definition: A sequence of trials with possible outcomes $E_1, E_2, \ldots (finite\ or\ infinite)$ is called Markov chain if the probabilities of sample sequences are defined by the above equation for $P\left(E_{j_0}, E_{j_1}, \ldots, E_{j_n}\right)$ in terms of the probability distribution $\{a_k\}$ for E_k at initial (zeroth) trial and fixed conditional probabilities p_{jk} of E_k given that E_j has occurred in the preceding trial.

The conditional probabilities p_{jk} are best represented in a matrix of transitions

$$P = \begin{bmatrix} p_{11} & p_{12} & p_{13} & \cdots \\ p_{21} & p_{22} & p_{23} & \cdots \\ \vdots & \vdots & \vdots & \vdots \\ \cdots & \cdots & \cdots & \cdots \end{bmatrix}$$

With some algebra, it can be shown that the probability of transition from state E_j to E_k in exactly $n\ steps$ is characterized by elements of a matrix Q obtained by matrix multiplication $Q = P^n$.

For example, if we have a system that can occupy four states, then the $p - matrix$ is 4x4. Note that rearranging the four states (i.e., renumbering) will result in shuffling of the matrix entries. Suppose for a 4-state system after a renumbering scheme, and we found that the transition matrix looked as below -

$$P = \begin{bmatrix} p_{11} & p_{12} & 0 & 0 \\ p_{21} & p_{22} & 0 & 0 \\ 0 & 0 & p_{33} & p_{34} \\ 0 & 0 & p_{43} & p_{44} \end{bmatrix}$$

What this would mean is that the system does not go from state 1 to state 3. The system transition behavior is "broken up" in $1 \leftrightarrow 2$ and $3 \leftrightarrow 4$. This has essentially "subdivided" space within which the system transitions. Such reduction to "neat" forms of the p-matrix has implications for limitations of system transitions. One such special form of p-matrix is referred to as "Canonical form," where the subdivisions of the transition space themselves cannot be further subdivided, i.e., you have represented it as a collection of "irreducible states." I will differ the details to graduate and undergraduate texts, such as one referred to earlier.

Emotional Inspiration

Markov chains were introduced and studied by Russian mathematician Andrey Markov more than 100 years ago in the early 20th century. Since then, the framework has found many interesting applications. The reader can search for the applications of Markov Chains on the internet and enjoy the spectrum of influence Markov chains have had and be amused. If you performed the search on Google, you would have relied on one of Markov chains' most impressive use – Serge Brin and Larry Page's application of Markov chains to web search! One can start with "The Five Greatest Applications of Markov Chains" by Philipp von Hilgers and Amy N. Langville (AMS article) for the first look.

A student of probability and statistics in the modern-day classroom is likely already aware of Markov chain's name before the first class. It is easy to engage in the study and scrutiny of the formalism when charged with an impressive application spectrum for the topic being discussed. I did not have to use Markov chains in my profession much to date, although room exists for such use. So, I had the privilege and what I call an "outsider's advantage" in going through Markov chains' study. In the first such skeptical look, I failed to be impressed with the use of p-matrix and formalism associated with classification of states. It seemed like a clever use of linear algebra in disguise. Representing probability calculations through matrix multiplication involving p-matrix seemed like an achievement in clean representation rather than something of fundamental character. I was looking for 'magic' that would happen after defining the p-matrix, and it was not happening.

Things that I saw represented clever observations that were enabled due to judiciously pulling over tools from linear algebra – and yes, I did feel the annoyance of someone turning over "row multiplied by column" thinking in matrix operations and writing matrix multiplications the "other way around." I was left with a feeling of being impressed with applications but not feeling charged due to the fundamental character of the framework. It is like the sentiment after reading Markov's application to Eugene Onegin (Alexander Pushkin's poem) – the first application presented by Markov himself! My feelings were like those discussed by Hilgers and Langville in their opening remarks about this application.

It took me a while to keep the skepticism aside and revisit the framework with a more open mind of a curious student because I did not need to use it in my work or teach the subject in my classroom. Only when I asked what effort it would take to populate the p-matrix for an application, that I was awakened to the intricacies. You would investigate the history for analysis using Markov chains. I asked myself how confident I would be that the historic data I would be using to calculate p-matrix would indeed fit the Markov hypothesis? – that the "next transition would depend *directly and only on* the current state"? I discussed this with Prof. S. Karnik from Georgia Tech in one of my numerous phone conversations. In that scrutiny and dialogue with self, all hell broke loose. I realized that I would not know if the next jump would be a function of the entire history, i.e., the function of a function (functional) or function of a point value? Or maybe two points? Or maybe a few points? If I simply counted the so-called "transitions" and assigned probability values in p-matrix from history, I would have already assumed that the process was Markov!

With comments from Prof. Karnik, it was like a flash: it seemed to me that Markov hypothesis is like the polar opposite of the law of Karma. In the law of Karma, the history of actions (your Karma) affects your evolution. In Markov hypothesis, the next state depends only on the current state. I suddenly woke up to the significance of the cliché I had heard several times – "live in the moment." I said to myself – "To achieve Nirvana, you essentially have to turn Markov!". I lost sleep over this internal dialogue and then wrote this poem after more than a month of soaking in that shock.

♦

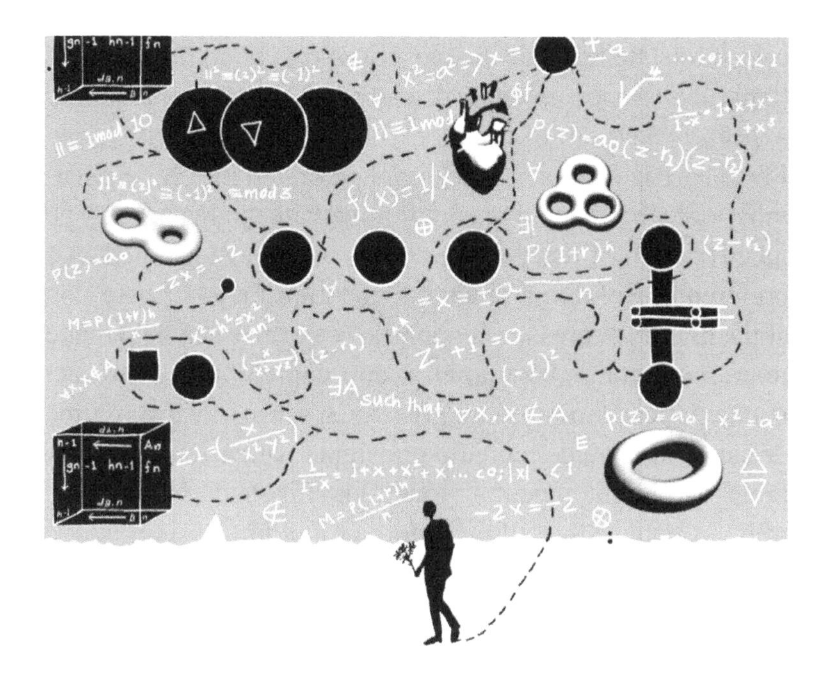

Closure

If you have survived the book to reach this page and intend to read the closure, I feel a bit more entitled to write freely about what I hope to accomplish in your reading of the book. This book was not written in the spirit of "mathematics can be fun," but I certainly hope you had fun reading it. I believe that mathematics can be hard, mathematics can be dry, mathematics can be frustrating, mathematics can be useful, mathematics can be useless, mathematics can be fun, and mathematics can be profound. On the same footing, mathematics can invoke emotional reactions, just as it can intellectually stimulate a person.

I wish to state here for the closure of this book that in emotional experience associated with mathematics, one should expect a spectrum of emotions just as with other things in life. There is no reason to be hooked on the idea of applicability or be bothered by lack of immediate applicability. The identification of that feature and its weightage is a personal preference. Solving a quadratic equation may not help you at the grocery store, solving matrices cleverly can help make impressive computer graphics, and contemplating abstract mathematical concepts can give you a sense of wasting time or can also provide incredible insights which seem comparable to enlightenment - your close encounter with "the truth." I believe that all the emotions and impressions above are well justified, and they are merely a reflection of who you are as an individual.

The pleasure of experiencing certainty in mathematical results can be worth desiring even when they do not have an immediate practical use or even when the truth laid out is too simple. That pleasure does not have to depend on the degree of difficulty in understanding or proving the result. One can happily live without knowing anything about Lebesgue integration, and knowing Riemann integration can give you some miserable hours as well. There is no reason for treating a favorite color on a different footing from a favorite mathematical object. The central theme I have carried in my presence at the abstract intersections all this time is that there is undoubtedly some room for emotions in learning and experiencing mathematics!

The emotional experience in learning and experiencing mathematics should be cherished without compromising the learning process. It should be made an integral part of the individual's learning process. Like any other subject, I also feel that mathematics should be learned knowing what you carry with you with 'all books closed' and what you *feel* about what you carry with you whenever you draw upon that knowledge. Unfortunately, the second part of knowing what we feel about new mathematics we learn is often ignored. We are trained to ignore – more so in mathematics than in other disciplines. If you find yourself at a place where reading the words mathematics and poetry in one place does not make you uncomfortable anymore, you are a little more open to any of such combinations after reading the book. I would be glad that this book helped make your presence at such abstract intersections pleasurable in whatever minuscule way.

I will close the book taking a bow to one of the revered personalities of the subject we can relate to since he impacted our thoughts from early school life and formative years as a mathematician and physicist. He is, of course, not the only mathematician to bow to, but yes, I do believe that more people might feel the influence he had on them than some of the other great mathematicians –

Newton

On the quiet greens of Grantham
Stood an ordinary-looking tree
Not knowing that its shadow would unlock
The mysteries of the universe and hand over the key

Suffering of a kid, the tree witnessed
Without the slightest of qualm
The domestic turmoil of his childhood, it knew
Prepared him to attain a heavenly calm

The truth had to transcend it all
When an apple from this tree had taken its spontaneous fall
The hungry son of God had resisted the instinct of a mortal
In that momentary pause
A seed was planted in his thought
And that was nothing short of a miracle
Like God's own whisper, with chortle

The Sun and the moon and stars and the galaxies
Had reflected upon the moment
The atomic cohesion of the material world
Had also envied this endowment

The Wolsthorpe Manor had risen
Above and beyond its existence as a mere shelter
The dark ages of beliefs were to end ...for which
The God had said, "Let there be light"
And then there was Newton
Born to change the mathematics of the universe
With divine-in-sight!

♦

Acknowledgments

If I have to be true to my emotions about what made this book possible and who are the contributors to my emotional journey in mathematics to this point, then the list is long. Writing this acknowledgment is indeed a difficult task due to this. The first and foremost are my parents, who encouraged me to pursue what I like. In particular, my father and grandfather, who had influenced my mathematical inclinations from early childhood, are worth mentioning separately. I am indebted to my parents for supporting me for one full year of self-study in mathematics after engineering graduation. This book would not have been possible without that exploration.

My mathematics teachers had a lot to do with all my emotional experiences in learning mathematics. In my eleventh-grade education, one name deserving special mention is the late Prof. C. S. Deshpande, the founder of Vidyalankar Institute in Mumbai. He kindled my interest in mathematics and influenced me as a person in my formative years. In the year of self-study after engineering, I was fortunate to have met Prof. Nitin Nitsure from the School of Mathematics, Tata Institute of Fundamental Research (T. I. F. R.), who was one of my most influential mathematics teachers. I am deeply indebted to him and Prof. Ravi Rao for nurturing my interest in pure mathematics exploration without hesitation of any kind. Despite being accomplished professional mathematicians, they were open to guiding me, an engineering student, for pure mathematics explorations in my self-study. My experience in the prestigious School of Mathematics, Tata Institute of Fundamental Research as a graduate student in pure mathematics uniquely shaped my views to make this book possible.

When it comes to making this book in print possible, three names stand out from the rest of my close friends and colleagues. Dr. Joseph Varghese showed confidence in me to compile these poems as a book for publication. Without valuable discussions with Dr. Varghese, I would probably not have compiled these poems in a book for publication. Prof. Satyajit Karnik is why I know the value of sitting on the beach at 2:30 am and engaging actively in internalizing mathematical results. His encouragement in pursuing this publication and the detailed scrutiny he provided for poems has enabled me to dissect my emotions and understanding of mathematical results in many instances. I would also like to thank Lauren Leonard for the encouragement and energy she brought to me while discussing many of these poems and providing a fresh perspective and valuable opinions. Last but certainly not least is the contribution from my daughter Shraddha Hardikar. She read my poems with exceptional patience and was always able to give me a teenager perspective with honesty, and suggest many improvements with constructive criticism. Finally, I am deeply indebted to my reviewers for reading the manuscript and providing detailed and encouraging reviews.

Despite all these valuable contributions and help, I am responsible for any errors in the book.

♦

Made in the USA
Monee, IL
07 February 2021